TOM JONES

A COMIC OPERA IN THREE ACTS

FOUNDED UPON FIELDING'S NOVEL

BY

ALEX. M. THOMPSON

AND

ROBERT COURTNEIDGE

LYRICS BY

CHAS. H. TAYLOR

MUSIC BY

EDWARD GERMAN

VOCAL SCORE - - - 15/- NET CASH

CHAPPELL & Co., Ltd.,
50 NEW BOND STREET, LONDON, W
NEW YORK SYDNEY

PRINTED IN GREAT BRITAIN BY
LOWE AND BRYDONE (PRINTERS) LIMITED, LONDON, N.W.10

Produced by Mr. ROBERT COURTNEIDGE

TOM JONES

DRAMATIS PERSONAE

Tom Jones (*a Foundling*)	Mr. C. Hayden Coffin
Mr. Allworthy (*a Somersetshire Magistrate*)	Mr. John Morley
Blifil (*his Nephew*)	Mr. Arthur Soames
Benjamin Partridge (*a Village Barber*)	Mr. Dan Rolyat
Squire Western (" *a fine Old English Gentleman* ")	Mr. Ambrose Manning
Gregory, Grizzle, Dobbin — *his Servants*	Mr. Jay Laurier, Mr. Walter L. Rignold, Mr. Reginald Crompton
Squire Cloddy, Pimlott, Tony — *friends of Squire Western*	Mr. Harry Cottell, Mr. D. Percival, Mr. W. Biddlecombe
An Officer	Mr. H. Welchman
Two Highwaymen	Messrs. Melville and Derrick
Post Boy	Mr. Woodin
Waiter	Mr. Carr Evans
Colonel Hampstead	Mr. Rupert Mar
Tom Edwards	Mr. Manners
Colonel Wilcox	Mr. Dalmuir
Honour (*Maid to Sophia*)	Miss Carrie Moore
Miss Western (*Squire Western's Sister*)	Miss Marie Daltra
Lady Bellaston (*a Lady of Quality*)	Miss Dora Rignold
Etoff (*her Maid*)	Miss Dorothy Ward
Hostess of the Inn at Upton	Miss Florence Parfrey
Bessie Wiseacre, Lettie Wheatcroft, Rosie Lucas — *Friends of Sophia*	Miss Minna Green, Miss Annie Heenan, Miss Cicely Courtneidge
Susan (*Serving Maid at Upton*)	Miss Maud Thornton
Betty, Peggy — *Waiting Maids*	Miss Mabel Newcombe, Miss Fay Temple
AND	
Sophia (*Squire Western's Daughter*)	Miss Ruth Vincent

SYNOPSIS OF SCENERY

Act	Scene	Artist
ACT I.	The Lawn at Squire Western's	*Stafford Hall*
ACT II.	The Inn at Upton	*Conrad Tritschler*
ACT III.	Ranelagh Gardens	*Conrad Tritschler*

TOM JONES

CONTENTS

ACT I

ACT II

ACT III

TOM JONES.

INTRODUCTION.

EDWARD GERMAN.

A JIG.
p STRINGS.

WOOD.
HORNS.
PIZZ.

sf
sf
BRASS.

sf
sf

sf
sf

1.
2.
OBOE.
B STRINGS.
p

1.
2.

TUTTI.
sf
sf
sf
sf

sf
rit.

C
ff a tempo

1.
2.
sf
sf

sf
sf

CODA.

Andante.

(Beat quick 6.)

D Andante ma non troppo. ♩.=50.

Largamente.

Segue Opening Chorus.

Nº 1. OPENING CHORUS.

A
sf
CYMB.
sf
CYMB.

(CURTAIN.)

sf
Ped.

CHORUS OF LADIES. (Sop.)
p
Don't you find the wea - ther charm - ing? Quite a warm Oc - to - ber
B
STRINGS. CLTS.
pp

LADS
day! Have you heard the news a - larm - ing? La - dy Bet - ty's run a -

Sop.
LADS.
Con.
-way!
Wife of gay Lord This-tle - down.
La-dy Bet-ty! who may she be?
Real-ly
OB.
FL.
TRIANGL.
LADS.
Sure 'tis all the talk in town! Bid-dy
now, and who may he be?
VIO. I.
LADS.
Prim's re-turn'd de-clar-ing That the dames at Ran-e-lagh All the

C
LADS
sea-son have been wear-ing Tif-fan - y and Taf - - fe - ta.
That the
FL. CL.
LADS
Pad-ua - soy in cha-ney green Is ev-'ry-where the
dames at Ran-e - lagh All the sea-son have been wear-ing Tif-fan-
pp
LADS
thing. So-phy Tiv-er-ton has been Pre - sent-ed to the King, Well-a-
-y and Taf-fe - ta, All the sea-son have been wear-ing Tif-fan - y and Taf-fe-

LADS
-day! Well-a-day a-well-a-day! Well-a-
-ta. All the sea-son have been wear-ing Tif-fan-y and Taf-fe-ta.
BRASS.
LADS
-day! and sure 'tis all the talk in town 'Tis all the talk in
'Tis all the talk in
D
LADS
town. Don't you find the wea-ther charm-ing? Quite a warm Oc-to-ber day. Have you
town. Don't you find the wea-ther charm-ing? Quite a warm Oc-to-ber day. Have you
OB.
STRINGS. WOOD. HORNS.

E
LADS
heard the news a - larm - ing? La - dy Bet - ty's run a - way Bid - dy
heard the news a - larm - ing? La - dy Bet - ty's run a - way Bid - dy
pp
sf
PIZZ.
LADS
Prim's re - turn'd de - clar - ing That the dames at Ran - e - lagh All the
Prim's re - turn'd de - clar - ing That the dames at Ran - e - lagh
PICC. FL.
ppp
LADS
sea - son have been wear - ing Tif - fan - y and Taf - fe - ta.
All the
ten.

F
LADS.
Bid - dy
sea - son have been wear - ing Tif - fan - y and Taf - fe - ta.
ten.
LADS.
Prim's re - turned de - clar - ing That the dames,
That the dames, the dames, the
ARCO
LADS.
That the dames at Ran - e - lagh All the sea - son have been
dames, That the dames at Ran - e - lagh All the sea - son have been

LADS.
wear - ing Tif - fan - y and Taf - fe - ta, All the sea - son have been
wear - ing Tif - fan - y and Taf - fe - ta, All the sea - son have been
LADS.
f
wear - ing Tif - fan - y and Taf - fe - ta.
f
wear - ing Tif - fan - y and Taf - fe - ta.
mf
BRASS.
Allegro moderato. = 112.
(Chorus of Huntsmen at back.)
Tenors.
LADS.
A - way! Gone a - way! Hark
Basses.
A - way! Gone a - way! Hark
f HORNS.
PIZZ.

HUN.
for - ward! A - way! Hark for - ward! Hark for - ward! A - way!
for - ward! A - way! Hark for - ward! Hark for - ward! A - way!
TRUMPET.
(strong accent.)
The fox is found, Fly horse and hound, But on her day I swear There
The fox is found, Fly horse and hound, But on her day I swear There
(strong accent.)
BRASS.
G
nev - er was horse to cov - er the ground Like the old grey mare.
nev - er was horse to cov - er the ground Like the old grey mare. Yoicks!
STRINGS.

HUN.
Ah!
Yoicks! There nev-er was horse to cov-er the ground, to cov-er the ground,
TRUMPET. HORN.
There nev-er was horse to cov-er the ground Like the old grey
There nev-er was horse to cov-er the ground Like the old grey
mare. Hark a-way! Hark a-way!
mare. Hark a-way! Hark a-way!
B.D.& CYMB.

H
SOLO.
And then we come to Bot-tom Spinney.
(CHORUS OF HUNTSMEN.)
HUN.
Hey fox!
Hey fox!
Animato.
PICC. FL.
STRINGS.
BRASS.

Hark! the hor-ses give a whin-ny,
HUN.
Grey fox!
Hi fox!
Sly fox!
Grey fox!
Hi fox!
Sly fox!

I
"Yoicks" says Har-ry the Whip he's found," Tal-ly Ho! and a-way we tear; And
HUN.
Tal-ly Ho! and a-way we tear;
Tal-ly Ho! and a way we tear;

CHORUS OF LADIES.
Hark
Hark
hard on the heels of the hind-most hound Comes Pat-ti-son's old grey mare.
HUN.
Comes Pat-ti-son's old grey mare.
Comes Pat-ti-son's old grey mare.
FL.
LADS.
to our spou - - ses, Hark!
to our spou - - ses, Hark!
"Yoicks!" says Har-ry, the Whip, "he's found" Tal-ly Ho! and a-way we tear.
HUN.
"Yoicks!" says Har-ry, the Whip, "he's found" Tal-ly Ho! and a-way we tear. And
"Yoicks!" says Har-ry, the Whip, "he's found" Tal-ly Ho! and a-way we tear. And

LADS.
to our spou - - ses, to our
to our spou - - ses, to our
HUN.
hard on the heels of the hind-most hound Comes Pat-ti-son's old grey mare, the
hard on the heels of the hind-most hound Comes Pat-ti-son's old grey mare, the
sf
p
rit.
J Allegro moderato.
LADS.
spou-ses hear - ken!
spou-ses hear - ken!
HUN.
sf
old grey mare The fox is found, Fly horse and hound, But
old grey mare The fox is found, Fly horse and hound, But
STRINGS.
6
6
Allegro moderato.
rit.
sf HORNS & BRASS.
PIZZ.

HUN.
on her day— I swear—— There nev-er was horse to cov-er the ground Like the
on her day— I swear—— There nev-er was horse to cov-er the ground Like the
HUN.
old grey mare. Ah!
old grey mare. Yoicks! Yoicks! There nev-er was horse to
HUN.
There nev-er was horse to
cov-er the ground, To cov-er the ground,—— There nev-er was horse to
sf

HUN.
cov - er the ground Like the old grey mare. Tal - ly -
cov - er the ground Like the old grey mare. Tal - ly -
K
HUN.
- ho! Tal - ly - ho!
- ho! Tal - ly - ho!
sf
STRINGS.
CL. (SUSTAIN.)
dim.
LADIES.
p
Hark! hark! our spou - ses Sharp their wits With con - ver - sa - tion As be - fits Their
OB.
pp

L
LADS.
state and sta - tion,
To ca -
As be - fits their state and sta - tion
PIZZ.
-rouse is Tru - ly an ex - treme - ly, And su - preme - ly
To ca - rouse is Tru - ly an ex - treme - ly, And su - preme - ly
Gen - tle - man - ly oc - cu - pa - tion.
Gen - tle - man - ly oc - cu - pa - tion.
HUN.
Tal - ly
Tal - ly

O
LAD^S.
HUN.
ho! Tal - ly ho! Tal - ly ho! Tal - ly ho! Tal - ly
ho! Tal - ly ho! Tal - ly ho! Tal - ly ho! Tal - ly
f STRINGS. WOOD. HORNS. TROMB.
LAD^S.
HUN.
ho! Tal - ly ho! Tal - ly ho! A -
ho! Tal - ly ho! Tal - ly ho! A -

P
LADS.
Don't you find the wea - ther charm - ing? Quite a
Don't you find the wea - ther charm - ing? Quite a
HUN.
-way The fox is found! Fly horse and hound, There
-way The fox is found! Fly horse and hound, There
STRINGS. WOOD. HORNS.
LADS.
warm Oc - to - ber day. Have you
warm Oc - to - ber day. Oc - to - ber day. Have you
HUN.
nev - er was horse to cov - er the ground like the old grey mare. The
nev - er was horse to cov - er the ground like the old grey mare. The
PIZZ.
ARCO

LADS.
heard the news a - larm - ing? La - dy Bet - ty's run a - way!
heard the news a - larm - ing? La - dy Bet - ty's run a - way!
HUN.
fox is found, Fly horse and hound. There nev - er was horse to cov - er the ground like the
fox is found, Fly horse and hound. There nev - er was horse to cov - er the ground like the
FL.
LADS.
Wife of gay Lord This - tle -
run a - way! Wife of gay Lord This - tle -
(to Ladies.)
HUN.
old grey mare. La - dy Bet - ty! who may she be?
old grey mare. La - dy Bet - ty! who may she be?

LAD.
-down. Sure 'tis all the talk in town. Bid-dy
-down. Sure 'tis all the talk in town. Bid-dy
HUN.
Real-ly now, and who may he be?
Real-ly now, and who may he be?
p
mf
cresc.
Q
f
LADS.
Prim's re-turn'd de-clar-ing That the dames
Prim's re-turn'd de-clar-ing That the dames, the dames,
(Huntsmen turn away impatiently.)
HUN.
There nev-er was horse to cov-er the ground There
There nev-er was horse to cov-er the ground, There
TIMP.

LADS.

That the dames at Ran - e -

the dames. That the dames at Ran - e -

HUN.

nev - er was horse to cov - er the ground. There nev - er was

nev - er was horse to cov - er the ground. There nev - er was

LADS.

- lagh All the sea - son have been wear - ing Tif - fa - ny and Taf - fe - ta, All the

- lagh All the sea - son have been wear - ing Tif - fa - ny and Taf - fe - ta, All the

HUN.

horse to cov - er the ground like the old

horse to cov - er the ground like the old

LADS.
sea-son have been wear-ing Tif-fa-ny and Taf-
sea-son have been wear-ing Tif-fa-ny and Taf-
HUN.
grey mare, like the old the old
grey mare, like the old the old
R Allegro molto.
LADS.
-fe-ta. Out up-on your "Hark a-
-fe-ta. Out up-on your "Hark a-
HUN.
grey mare, Hark a-way, a-way, a-way a-way a-
grey mare, Hark a-way, a-way, a-way, a-way a-
Allegro molto.
TUTTI.
sf

LADS.
-way" Out up - on your "Hark a-
-way" Out up - on your "Hark a-
HUN.
-way. Hark a-way, a-way, a-way, a-way, a-
-way. Hark a-way, a-way, a-way, a-way, a-
sf

S
LADS.
-way;" a-way!"
-way;" a-way!"
HUN.
-way, a-way!
-way, a-way!
ff

sf
sf

No. 2. SONG.–(Squire Western) and CHORUS.

Cue. WESTERN:–"I be going to tell the ladies."

WES.
sud-den-ly there came from a cop - pice, so clear, The call of a cuck - oo in
o-ther maid said "Phoe - be, you stay_where you be, That cuck - oo baint up to no
p
B
song. It as - ton-ish-èd those pret-ty maids the
good." 'Tis, for pret-ty maids to run a-way when
CL.
sf
cuck-oo for to hear On a Jan - u-air-y morn - ing in Zum-mer-zet -
cuck-oo sings so clear On a Jan - u-air-y morn - ing in Zum-mer-zet -
sf HORN.
p
f
C
a tempo
-sheer, On a Jan - - u-air-y morn-ing, in Zum-mer-zet - sheer.
-sheer, On a Jan - - u-air-y morn-ing, in Zum-mer-zet - sheer.
CHO.
On a Jan - - u-air-y morn-ing, in Zum-mer-zet - sheer.
On a Jan - - u-air-y morn-ing, in Zum-mer-zet - sheer.
On a Jan-u-air - y morn - ing, in Zum-mer-zet - sheer.
On a Jan-u-air - y morn - ing, in Zum-mer-zet - sheer.
f TUTTI.
a tempo

ENCORE.
WES.
FL.
f
TRIANG.
p
D
3. But that pret-ty maid went seek-ing the_ cop-pice a-lone,
OB. WITH VOICE.
STRINGS.
pp
As her fol-ly led her so for to do, her so for to
CHO.
Led her so for to do.
Led her so for to do.
p meno mosso
do, And now she goes la-ment-ing and mak-ing a
pp

E
WES.
moan, That cuck - oos in win - ter baint true.
CL.
WES.
'Tis a sor - ry month for sil - ly maids when cuck - oo sings so
sf
F
WES.
clear On a Jan - u - air - y morn - ing in Zum - mer - zet -
sf HORN.
p
WES.
f
-sheer, On a Jan - - u - air - y morn - ing in Zum - mer - zet - sheer. With a
f
On a Jan - - u - air - y morn - ing in Zum - mer - zet - sheer.
CHO.
f
On a Jan - u - air - y morn - ing in Zum - mer - zet - sheer.
f TUTTI.

G Animato.
WES.
fol de rol, lol de rol, fol de rol, lol de rol, Sor-ry month for sil-ly
FL.CL.
Animato.
PIZZ.
Allargando
maid-ens When cuck-oo sings clear, On a
CHO.
When cuck-oo sings clear, When cuck-oo sings clear, On a
When cuck-oo sings clear, When cuck-oo sings clear, On a
Allargando
TUTTI.
a tempo
rall.
Jan-u-air-y morning, in Zummer-zet-sheer. With a fal, la, la, la.
Jan-u-air-y morning, in Zummer-zet-sheer. With a fal, la, la, la, la, la, la, la.
Jan-u-air-y morning, in Zummer-zet-sheer. With a fal, la, la, la, la, la, la, la.
a tempo
rall.

No. 3. SONG.–(Tom) and CHORUS.

Cue. WESTERN:–"Sing us a Song."

TOM.

I have no steed, nor sturdy hack To
I have not e'er a blunderbuss Nor

pp STRINGS. CLT.

pp

Ped. * Ped. *

A

TOM.

sit astride, I hear the music
gun, to kill, The pheasant crows, and

CHO.

To sit astride.
Nor gun to kill.

To sit astride.
Nor gun to kill.

f TUTTI.

pp STRINGS.

TOM.

Hark, the pack! Down countryside, And
runneth puss O' yonder hill, I

CHO.

f

Down countryside,
O' yonder hill,

f

Down countryside,
O' yonder hill,

f TUTTI.

p

TOM.
fain would hunt - ing go, a - lack! I have no steed, or grey, or black, Or
fain would shoot - ing go, and thus I sigh for bur - ly blun - der-buss, Or

B
TOM.
pp
sor-rel, or brown, or pied! O give him a horse or
gun of my own, to kill! O give him a gun or
STRINGS.
rit.
FL.
pp a tempo
TRIANG.

TOM.
grey, or black, or sor-rel, or brown, or pied! For shall it be said a
blun - der-buss, And set him up-on the hill! For shall it be said a

TOM.
f
Som - er - set lad Has no horse, no horse to
Som - er - set lad Has no gun, no gun to

C
TOM.
ride?
kill?
O give him a
O give him a
CHO.
O give him a horse, or grey, or black, or
O give him a gun, or blun - der-buss And
TUTTI.
TOM.
horse.
gun
shall it be said a
CHO.
sor-rel, or brown, or pied. For shall it be said a
set him up on the hill. For shall it be said a

TOM.
Som-er-set lad Has no horse, no horse to
Som-er-set lad Has no gun, no gun, to
CHO.
Som-er-set lad Has no horse, no horse to
Som-er-set lad Has no gun, no gun, to
Som-er-set lad Has no horse, no horse to
Som-er-set lad Has no gun, no gun, to
D
ENCORE. (2nd time.)
TOM.
ride?
kill?
CHO.
ride?
kill?
ride?
kill?
f
TUTTI.
Ped.
1.
2.
TOM.
CHO.
sf
sf
sf
rall.

E
Andante. ♩.=92.
TOM.
West Country lad, what lack ye yet? A maid to kiss.
CHO.
A maid to kiss.
A maid to kiss.
HORN.
CL. SUST.
pp
No maid to love me have I met And all's a-miss.
And all's a-miss.
And all's a-miss.
Allegro moderato. ♩.=126.
I look a-side at Sue, and Bet, And
WOOD.

TOM.
CHO.
cresc.
Kate and Siss— And fain would court-ing go, And yet I
And Kate and Siss;
And Kate and Siss;
BRASS.
cresc.
HORN SUS.
have no maid with eyes of jet, Or ha-zel, or blue, I
BRASS.
F
wis!
O
dim
molto
He has no maid with eyes of jet— He has no maid with eyes of
He has no maid with eyes of
(Steady time.)

pp
TOM.
Give him a maid with eyes of jet, Or ha-zel or blue I wis! For
jet, eyes of jet, eyes of jet, he has no maid with eyes of
CHO.
ppp
jet, eyes of jet, eyes of jet, he has no maid with eyes of
ppp STRINGS. FL.
TRIANG.
Ped. * Ped. *
TOM.
shall it be said a Som-er-set lad Has no maid, no maid to
f
jet to kiss, he has no maid to kiss, no maid to
CHO.
jet to kiss, he has no maid to kiss, no maid to
Ped. * Ped. *

G
TOM.
kiss: O give him a
CHO.
kiss. O give him a maid with eyes of jet, Or
kiss. O give him a maid with eyes of jet, Or
f TUTTI.
Ped. * Ped. *
TOM.
maid. Shall it be said a
CHO.
ha - zel or blue I wis, For shall it be said a
ha - zel or blue I wis, For shall it be said a

TOM.
Som - er - set lad
Has no maid
to
CHO.
Som - er - set lad
Has no maid
to
Som - er - set lad
Has no maid
to
TOM.
kiss?
CHO.
kiss?
kiss?
Animato.

Nº 4. SONG.– (Sophia.)

Cue. SOPHIA:–"Oh, what is the use of wondering."

Animato.
SO.
word, Thus heart to heart a - cross the si - lence calls;
OB. WITH VOICE.
STGS.
The voice of mine So tim - o - rous in tone, I
cresc.
won - der if up - on his ear it falls
cresc.
But as a seem-ing ec-ho of his own!
B
rit.
a tempo
p
He
rit
p
a tempo
HORN.
CELLO.

C
SO.
loves me so, I know I know! But when we are as - un - der, Does
p STGS.
he for-get? I trow not, yet I won-der, O I won-der I
f rit.
BRASS
f rit.
trow not, yet I won - der.
p
a tempo
D
ENCORE.
I
colla voce
STGS.
p
pp
VIO. I.
a tempo
mf
Animato.
trem-ble at his look, My burn - ing eyes Fain would I droop to hide
HORN SUST.
pp

SO.
the sud-den flame. He scans my cheek, and turns a - way and sighs,
VIO.I.
HORNS BRASS.
mf
CELLO PICC.
Animato.
And takes the blush of love for naught but maid - - - en shame. I won-der if 'twere
OB.
p
CL.
STGS.
wise to let him see That ev-'ry mo - ment by his side is bliss. I
won - der if 'twere mai-den-ly To give an' he should ask for it
f

SO.
E
a tempo
A kiss. He loves me so, I know, I know, But
rit.
a tempo
STGS.
HORN.
CELLO.
when we are a-sun-der, Does he for-get? I trow not, yet I won-der, Oh I
BRASS.
accel.
allargando
won-der Does he for-get? I trow not, Ah!
p rit.
Yet I won - der
STGS.
colla voce
FL. CL.
rit.
attacca.

INTERLUDE.

No. 4a

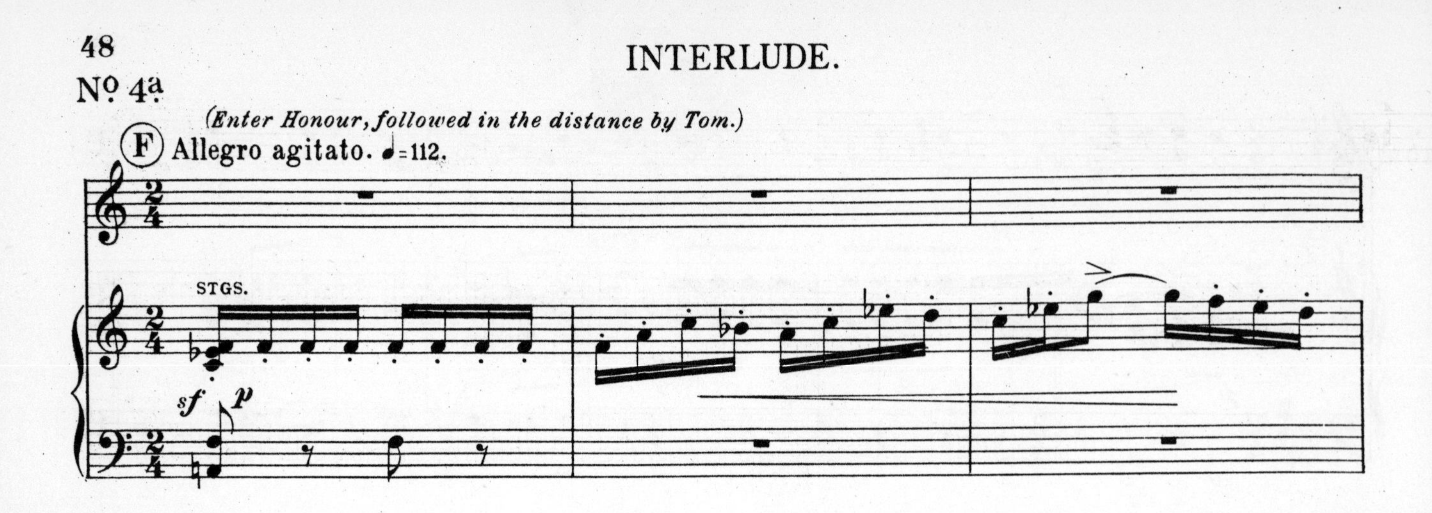

TOM.
TOM.
You
f
sf
PIZZ.
G
Recit.
SOPHIA.
a tempo
Animato.
TOM.
sent for me? Ah yes! have I dis - turb'd you, pray? For-give me! Ah
Recit.
p a tempo
STGS.
HORN. CL.
Allegro molto. ♩=144.
dear! such dis - tur - bance Sweet be - yond com -
FL. WITH VOICE.
- pare With an - y peace I know

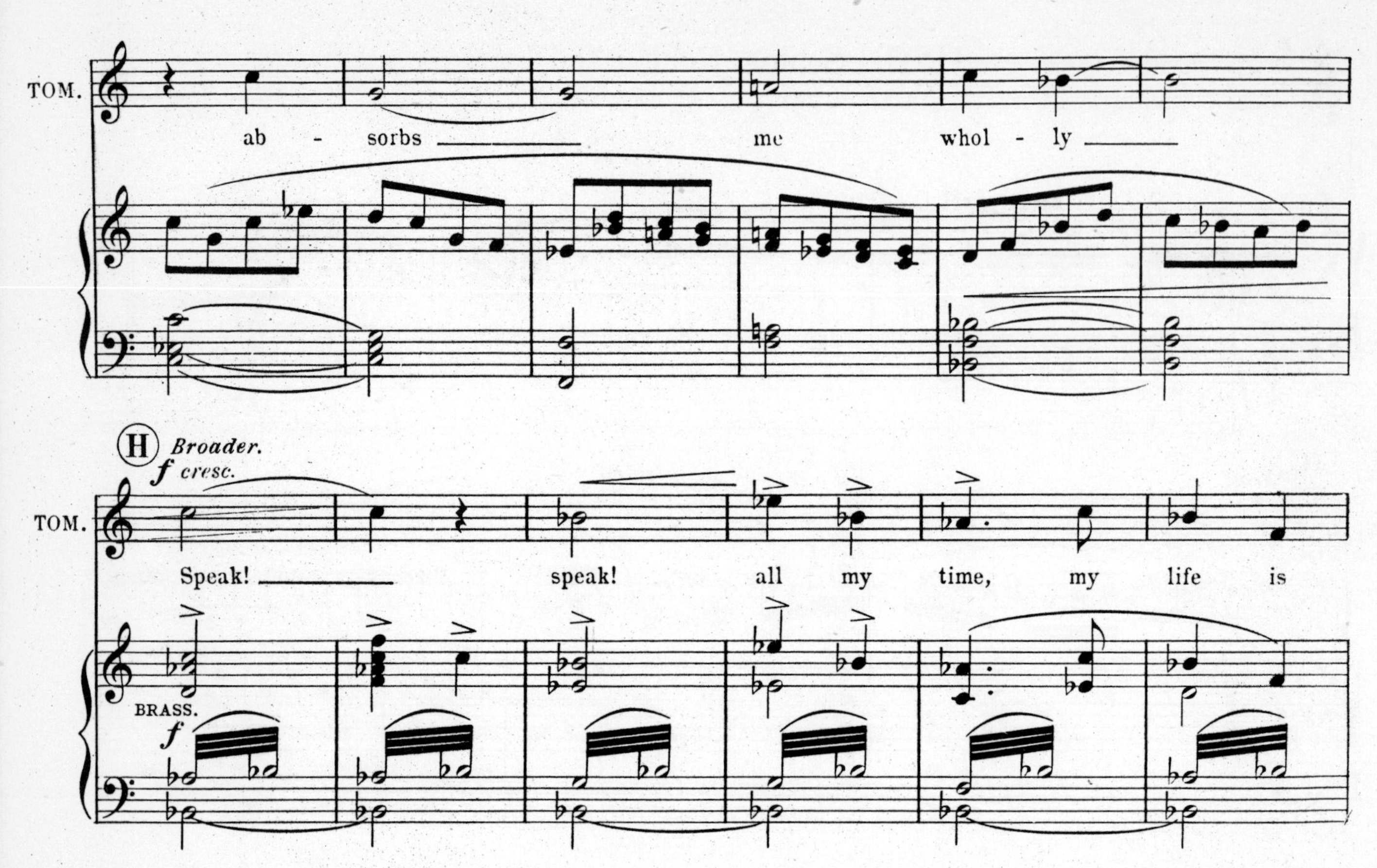
TOM.
ab - sorbs me whol - ly
H
Broader.
f cresc.
TOM.
Speak! speak! all my time, my life is
BRASS.
f

TOM.
yours!
SOPHIA.
Take care! We must make
WOOD HORNS.
ff
p

ad lib.
TOM.
SO.
pp
haste, Then let us make haste, slow - ly.
STGS. HORNS
pp
Ped.
segue

No 5. TRIO.– (Sophia, Honour and Tom.)

I
SO.
Tem-pus fu-git is the an-swer
We are vers'd in La-tin lore
FL. WITH VOICE.
SO.
Time is not a ne-cro-man-cer. Time's a cheat and noth-ing more.
HON.
TOM.
Time's a cheat and noth-ing
Animato.
SO.
HON.
Tem-pus fu-git is the an-swer
We are vers'd in La-tin
TOM.
more.
Tem-pus fu-git is the an-swer.
Animato.

SO.
HON.
TOM.
We are versed in La - tin lore— Time is but a cheat, is but a
lore. Time's a cheat, and no - thing
O Time is but a cheat, Time is but a cheat
cheat, a cheat and no - thing more, and no - thing
more, and no - thing more, Time's a cheat,
Time's a cheat and no - thing more, and no - thing more, and no - thing
CL.
J
Allegro. (a la Valse.)
more, and no - thing more. Fool - ish
Time's a cheat. Fool - ish
more, and no - thing more. Ah!
STGS.
TAMB.

SO.
prov - erb, Time works won - ders, 'Ere 'tis run he turns the
HON.
prov - erb, Time works won - ders, 'Ere it is run he turns the
TOM.
CL.
SO.
glass; Speed-ing thus the hour that sun - ders Hap-py
HON.
glass the glass, Speed-ing thus the hour that sun - ders Hap-py
TOM.
lov - er, lov - ing
K
SO.
lov - ing lass, Ah!
HON.
lov - er, lov - ing lass, Fool - ish prov - erb, Time works
TOM.
Fool - ish prov - erb, Time works
BRASS.

SO.
Ah! Hap - py the
HON.
won - ders, Ere 'tis run he turns the glass, turns the
TOM.
won - ders, Ere 'tis run he turns the glass, turns the

SO.
lov - er, Hap - py lov - - er And his lov - - ing
HON.
glass, Hap - py lov - - er And his lov - - ing
TOM.
glass, Hap - - py lov - er And his lov - - ing

SO.
lass.
HON.
lass.
TOM.
lass.

L
A Tempo primo. Moderato.
SO.
TOM.
Cru - el words Fes - ti - na
A Tempo primo. Moderato.
(Beat 3.)
sf
rit.
♩=120.
p
STGS.
len - te
To a lov - er and his lass!
Cru - el words Fes - ti - na len - te
To a lov - er and his
Hearts im - pa - tient grow at twen - ty
When old Tem - pus tilts the
lass!
Hearts im - pa - tient grow at twen - ty

SO.
glass. Sands run slow - ly to their sor - row;
TOM.
When old Tem - pus tilts the glass. Sands run slow - ly to their
SO.
Drag the hours that keep them twain, Seems a week till hap - py
TOM.
sor - row; Drag the hours that keep them twain,
FL. WITH VOICE.
SO.
mor - row Brings them to the tryst a - gain.
TOM.
Seems a week till hap - py mor - row Brings them, brings them to the tryst a -

SO.
HON.
TOM.
Tem-pus fu-git? Nay, he creep-eth, When he should get on a
-gain. Tem-pus fu-git? Nay, he creep-eth,
When he should get on a-pace, Time is but a cheat, is but a
pace! Time's a cheat in a-ny
O Time is get-ting old, Time is get-ting old,
mf
dim.
p
rit.
pp
cheat a cheat in a-ny case, in a-ny case, in a-ny
case, in a-ny case, Time's a cheat, Time's a cheat,
Time's a cheat in a-ny case, in a-ny case, in a-ny case, in a-ny
CL.

ENCORE.
M
Allegro. (a la Valse.)
SO.
HON.
TOM.
case.
Fool-ish prov - erb, Time works won - ders, Ere 'tis
Fool-ish prov - erb, Time works won - ders, Ere it is
case.
Ah!
STGS.
CL.
TAMB.
run he turns the glass; Speed-ing thus the hour that sun-ders Hap-py
run he turns the glass; the glass, Speed-ing thus the hour that sun-ders Hap-py
lov-er, lov-ing lass.
lov - ing lass.
N
Ah!
lov - er, lov-ing lass. Fool-ish prov - erb, Time works won - ders, Ere 'tis
Fool-ish prov - erb, Time works won - ders, Ere 'tis
BRASS.

SO.
HON.
TOM.
Ah! Hap-py the lov-er, Hap-py lov-er and his
run he turns the glass, turns the glass, Hap-py lov-er and his
run he turns the glass, turns the glass, Hap-py lov-er and his
O
Piu Vivo.
lov-ing lass. Ah!
lov-ing lass. Tem-pus fu-git. Nay, he
lov-ing lass. Tem-pus fu-git.
Piu Vivo.
HORNS SUS.
creep-eth, creep-eth on a-pace! Nay, nay, he creep-eth on a-
Nay, nay, he creep-eth on a-

P
f Brillante.
SO.
ON.
OM.
Ah! Ah! Ah! Time's a
-pace! Ah! Time's a
-pace! Ah! Time's a
f
ff
BRASS.
Strict time.
cheat in a - ny case, in a - ny, a - ny
cheat in a - ny case, in a - ny, a - ny
cheat in a - ny case, in a - ny, a - ny
ff
Molto Allegro.
case.
case.
case.
Molto Allegro.
TUTTI.
Brillante.
sf

No. 6. ENSEMBLE.–(Honour and Gregory.)

(with Betty, Peggy, Grizzle, and Dobbin.)

"THE BARLEY MOW."

Cue. GREGORY:–"While I do sit and drink it under the green bough."

HON.
zwing - in' zign zo all may zee,
A
GR.
A
BET.& PEG.
p
Un - der a green bough,
GRI.& DOB.
FL.
p
HON.
road - side inn, zo znug with - in, Vur lads that fol - low the plough. We'll
GR.
road - side inn, zo znug with - in, Vur lads that fol - low the plough. We'll
BET.& PEG.
We'll
GRI.& DOB.
We'll
BRASS.

A

HON: drink to the Bar - ley Mow, Drink to the Bar - ley Mow.

GR. drink to the Bar - ley Mow, Drink to the Bar - ley Mow. In a

BET.& PEG. drink to the Bar - ley Mow, Drink to the Bar - ley Mow.

GRI.& DOB. drink to the Bar - ley Mow, Drink to the Bar - ley Mow.

S. DRUM.

Allegro. ♩=132.

HON. A quaart pot.

GR. quaart pot. A

BET.& PEG. BETTY. A pint pot. PEGGY. A nip-per-kin.

GRI.& DOB. GRIZZLE. A pint pot. DOBBIN. A nip-per-kin.

Allegro. ♩=132.

p

PIZZ.

HON. A pip-per-kin. Un - der a green bough. We'll

GR. pip-per-kin. Un - der a green bough. We'll

BET. & PEG. Un - der a green bough. We'll

GRI. & DOB. Un - der a green bough. We'll

STGS. WOOD HORNS.

TUTTI.

B Allegro giocoso. ♩. 112.

HON. drink to the Bar - ley Mow, Hey, and ho, and all be mer-ry, We'll

GR. drink to the Bar - ley Mow, Hey, and ho, and all be mer-ry, We'll

BET. & PEG. drink to the Bar - ley Mow, Hey, and ho, and all be mer-ry, We'll

GRI. & DOB. drink to the Bar - ley Mow, Hey, and ho, and all be mer-ry, We'll

Allegro giocoso. ♩. 112.

STGS. WOOD HORNS.

HON.
drink to the Bar - ley Mow, With a hey, ho, dum-ble down der-ry, We'll
GR.
drink to the Bar - ley Mow, With a hey, ho, dum-ble down der-ry, We'll
BET.& PEG.
drink to the Bar - ley Mow, With a hey, ho, dum-ble down der-ry, We'll
GRI.& DOB.
drink to the Bar - ley Mow, With a hey, ho, dum-ble down der-ry, We'll
TUTTI.
sf
C
HON.
drink to the Bar - ley Mow, the Bar - ley, Bar - ley Mow.
GR.
drink to the Bar - ley Mow, the Bar - ley, Bar - ley Mow. Oc -
p
BET.& PEG.
drink to the Bar - ley Mow, the Bar - ley, Bar - ley Mow.
GRI.& DOB.
drink to the Bar - ley Mow, the Bar - ley, Bar - ley Mow.
STGS.

HON.
Vur
GR.
-to - ber ale zo brown we'll brew.
BET.&
PEG.
p
Un - der a green bough,
GRI.&
DOB.
p
HON
var - mer's man and trav'- ler too,
Oc -
GR.
Oc -
BET.&
PEG.
GRI.&
DOB.
p
Un - der a green bough.
p

HON.
-to - ber brew, an' plen - ty too, Vur lads that fol - low the plough. We'll
GR.
-to - ber brew, an' plen - ty too, Vur lads that fol - low the plough. We'll
BET. & PEG.
We'll
GRI. & DOB.
We'll
D
HON.
drink to the Bar - ley Mow, Drink to the Bar - ley Mow.
GR.
drink to the Bar - ley Mow, Drink to the Bar - ley Mow. In a
BET. & PEG.
drink to the Bar - ley Mow, Drink to the Bar - ley Mow.
GRI. & DOB.
drink to the Bar - ley Mow, Drink to the Bar - ley Mow.
S. DRUM.

Allegro. ♩=132.
HON.
a 'ogs - 'ead.
GR.
'ogs - 'ead.
A
BETTY.
PEGGY.
BET. & PEG.
A gal-lon jar.
A quaart pot.
GRIZZLE.
DOBBIN.
GRI. & DOB.
A gal-lon jar.
A quaart pot.
Allegro. ♩=132.
pp
HON.
A pint pot.
GR.
pint pot.
BETTY.
PEGGY.
BET. & PEG.
A nipperkin.
A pipperkin.
GRIZZLE.
DOBBIN.
GRI. & DOB.
A nipperkin.
A pipperkin.

⁜ In case of encore, the symphony repeats from here— the voices joining at ⁜ on page 71.

HON.
hey, ho, dum-ble down der-ry, We'll drink to the Bar-ley Mow, the
GR.
hey, ho, dum-ble down der-ry, We'll drink to the Bar-ley Mow, the
BET. & PEG.
hey, ho, dum-ble down der-ry, We'll drink to the Bar-ley Mow, the
GRI. & DOB.
hey, ho, dum-ble down der-ry, We'll drink to the Bar-ley Mow, the
TUTTI.
sf
F
HON.
Bar-ley, Bar-ley Mow. Come Par-son, Pack-man,
GR.
Bar-ley, Bar-ley Mow. Come Par-son, Pack-man,
BET. & PEG.
Bar-ley, Bar-ley Mow.
GRI. & DOB.
Bar-ley, Bar-ley Mow.
STGS.
p

HON.
Herd, or Hind. An e - qual wel-come all shall vind
GR.
Herd, or Hind. An e - qual wel-come all shall vind
BET. & PEG.
p
Un-der a green bough.
GRI. & DOB.
p
Un-der a green bough.
p
HON.
Come Par - son, Hind, or Gen - tle-kind, Or
GR.
Come Par - son, Hind, or Gen - tle-kind, Or
BET. & PEG.
p
Un-der a green bough.
GRI. & DOB.
p
Un-der a green bough.

HON.
lads that fol - low the plough, We'll drink to the Bar - ley Mow, Drink
GR.
lads that fol - low the plough, We'll drink to the Bar - ley Mow, Drink
BET. & PEG.
We'll drink to the Bar - ley Mow, Drink
GRI. & DOB.
We'll drink to the Bar - ley Mow, Drink
G
Allegro. ♩=132.
HON.
to the Bar - ley Mow, A o - cean.
GR.
to the Bar - ley Mow, In a o - cean.
BETTY.
BET. & PEG.
to the Bar - ley Mow, A
GRIZZLE.
GRI. & DOB.
to the Bar - ley Mow, A riv - er.
S. DRUM.
Allegro. ♩=132.
pp

HON.
A gal-lon jar.
GR.
A gal-lon jar.
BET. & PEG.
PEGGY.
riv - er. A 'ogs - 'ead.
GRI. & DOB.
DOB.
GRIZ.
A 'ogs - 'ead. A
HON.
A nipperkin.
GR.
A nipper-kin.
BET. & PEG.
BET.
PEG.
A quaart pot. A pint pot.
GRI. & DOB.
DOB.
GRIZ.
quaart pot. A pint pot. A
OB.
CL.

H
HON.
A nipperkin, a pipperkin, a nipperkin, a
GR.
A o - cean, a riv - er, a 'ogs - 'ead, a
BET. & PEG.
BET.
BOTH.
A pipperkin, a nipperkin, a pipperkin, a nipperkin, a
GRI. & DOB.
BOTH.
pipperkin. A o - cean, a riv - er, a 'ogs - 'ead, a
FL.
HON.
pipperkin, a nipper-kin, a pipper-kin, a nipperkin, a pipperkin, a
GR.
gal-lon jar, a quaart pot, a pint pot, a nipperkin, a
BET. & PEG.
pipperkin, a nipper-kin, a pipper-kin, a nipperkin, a pipperkin, a
GRI. & DOB.
gal-lon jar, a quaart pot, a pint pot, a nipperkin, a

HON.
nip-per-kin, a pip-per-kin,
A
GR.
pip-per-kin, a nip-per-kin, a pip-per-kin, a nip-per-kin, a pip-per-kin,
BET. & PEG.
nip-per-kin, a pip-per-kin,
A
GRI. & DOB.
pip-per-kin, a nip-per-kin, a pip-per-kin, a nip-per-kin, a pip-per-kin,
I
HON.
f
nip-per-kin, a pip-per-kin, a nip-per-kin, a pip-per-kin, nip-per-kin, a pip-per-kin, a
GR.
f
A nip-per-kin, a pip-per-kin, a
BET. & PEG.
f
nip-per-kin, a pip-per-kin, a nip-per-kin, a pip-per-kin, nip-per-kin, a pip-per-kin, a
GRI. & DOB.
f
A nip-per-kin, a pip-per-kin, a
sf p STGS.
TUTTI.

f *accel.*

HON.
nip-per-kin, a pip-per-kin, a nip-per, nip-per, nip-per, nip-per, nip-per, nip-per, nip-per, nip-per,

f

GR.
nip-per-kin, a pip-per-kin, a nip-per, nip-per, nip-per, nip-per, nip-per, nip-per, nip-per, nip-per,

f

BET. & PET.
nip-per-kin, a pip-per-kin, a nip-per, nip-per, nip-per, nip-per, nip-per, nip-per, nip-per, nip-per,

f

GRI. & DOB.
nip-per-kin, a pip-per-kin, a nip-per, nip-per, nip-per, nip-per, nip-per, nip-per, nip-per, nip-per,

f *accel.*

slower *f* (J) Allegro giocoso. ♩.=112. *fp*

HON.
pip-per-kin, Un-der a green bough. We'll drink to the Bar-ley

f *fp*

GR.
pip-per-kin, Un-der a green bough. We'll drink to the Bar-ley

f *fp*

BET. & PET.
pip-per-kin, Un-der a green bough. We'll drink to the Bar-ley

f *fp*

GRI. & DOB.
pip-per-kin, Un-der a green bough. We'll drink to the Bar-ley

Allegro giocoso. ♩.=112.

f *sf* PICC. *fp* STGS. WOOD HORNS.

STGS. WOOD HORNS. TUTTI

HON.
Mow, Hey, and ho, and all be merry, We'll drink to the Bar - ley Mow, With a
GR.
Mow, Hey, and ho, and all be merry, We'll drink to the Bar - ley Mow, With a
BET. & PEG.
Mow, Hey, and ho, and all be merry, We'll drink to the Bar - ley Mow, With a
GRI. & DOB.
Mow, Hey, and ho, and all be merry, We'll drink to the Bar - ley Mow, With a
HON.
hey, ho, dumble down der-ry, We'll drink to the Bar - ley Mow, the Bar - ley,
GR.
hey, ho, dumble down der-ry, We'll drink to the Bar - ley Mow, the Bar - ley,
BET. & PEG.
hey, ho, dumble down der-ry, We'll drink to the Bar - ley Mow, the Bar - ley,
GRI. & DOB.
hey, ho, dumble down der-ry, We'll drink to the Bar - ley Mow, the Bar - ley,
sf
BRASS.

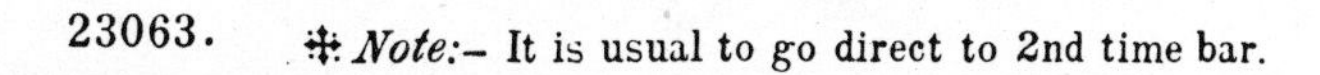
❈ *Note:-* It is usual to go direct to 2nd time bar.

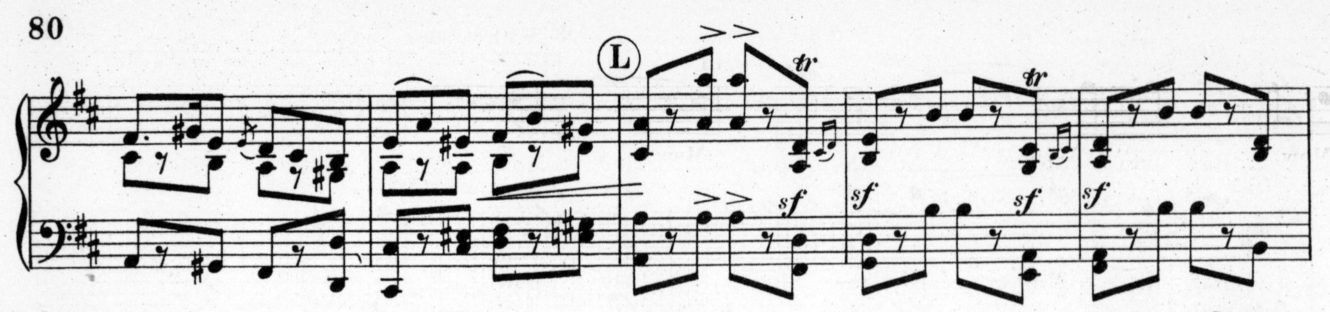
L
tr
tr
sf
sf
sf
sf

M
sf
sf
sf

N

O
accel.
f

TUTTI.
sf
Ped.
sff

Nº 7. MADRIGAL.—(Sophia, Honour, Tom and Alworthy.)

Cue. TOM:– "I am in no haste to find the light."

SO.
HON.
TOM.
AL.
mf
strong." When he thinks he most dis - cov-ers, Blind - est all the gods a - mong, Blind - est
strong." When he thinks he most dis - cov-ers, Blind - est all the gods a - mong, Yes,
strong." When he thinks he most dis - cov-ers, Blind - est all the gods a - mong, the gods a -
strong." When he thinks he most dis - cov-ers, Blind - est all the gods a - mong, Blind - est
all the gods a - mong, With a fal la la
blind - est all the gods a - mong, a - mong, With a fal la
-mong, Yes, blind - est all the gods a - mong, With a fal la
all the gods a - mong, the gods a - mong, the gods a - mong, With a fal la
f
pp
FL.
PIZZ.

A
SO.
la, With a fal la la la la la la la.
HON.
la, With a fal la la.
TOM.
la, With a fal la la. Hold - ing, lead him in kind fash - ion, Shield him
AL.
la, With a fal la la la.
ARCO.
SO.
HON.
TOM.
in such gen - tle wise,
AL.
That no sud-den gust of pas-sion Tear the ban-dage from his

B
Animato.
SO.
He will
HON.
Once des - troyéd Love's il - lu - sion - Sad for ye an it be - fall, He will
TOM.
He will
AL.
eyes. Ah Ah He will
FL.
Animato.
SO.
fly off in con-fu-sion, he will fly off in con-fu-sion, And es - cape for good and
HON.
fly off in con-fu-sion, he will fly off in con-fu-sion, And es - cape for good and
TOM.
fly, he will fly off in con-fu-sion, And es - cape for good and
AL.
fly, he will fly off in con-fu-sion, And es - cape for good and
23063

SO.
all, Will fly off in con-fu-sion, And es-cape for good and all. With a fal la la
ION.
all, es-cape, es - cape for good and all. Ah!
OM.
all, es-cape, es - cape for good and all. With a fal la
AL.
all, es-cape, es - cape for good and all. With a fal la
ff
pp
f
PIZZ.
C
SO.
la, With a fal la la la, With a fal la la la fal la la fal la la
ION.
With a fal la la fal la la fal la
OM.
la, With a fal la la la la la la fal la la fal la
AL.
la, With a fal la la la la la la fal la la fal la
ARCO.

Broader.
SO.
la la la la la la la la la la la la,With a fal la la la la la la.
HON.
la fal la la, With a fal la la la la la la. But at
TOM.
la fal la la, With a fal la la la la la la.
AL.
la fal la la, With a fal la la la la la la.
Broader.
FL. CL.
a tempo
SO.
HON.
lov-ers' sep-ar-a-tion Pi-ty in his bo-som starts.
TOM.
Learn ye then for con-so-
AL.
OB.
a tempo

D
SO.
HON.
TOM.
AL.
p
Done my dit_ty, here is yet a Par_a_dox_
Done my dit_ty, here is yet a Par_a_dox_
pp
_la_tion, Love loves mend-ing bro - ken hearts, bro - ken hearts.
_ to_fit the end: "Love must e'en break hearts to get a Store of bro_ken hearts to
_ to_fit the end: "Love must e'en break hearts to get a Store of bro_ken hearts to

ENCORE.
animato
E
SO.
HON.
TOM.
AL.
mend." Here's a par-a-dox, Here's a par-a-dox for lov - ers: O
Here's a par-a-dox, Here's a par-a-dox for lov - ers: O
ff animato
PIZZ.
Love must e'en break hearts to get a Store of bro-ken hearts to mend. With a fal la la
Love must e'en break hearts to get a Store of bro-ken hearts to mend.
Love must e'en break hearts to get broken hearts to mend.
dim.
rit.
a tempo pp (Not too fast)
ARCO.

F
(Strict time.)
SO.
HON.
TOM.
AL.
la, With a fal la la la,
With a fal la la
With a fal la
With a fal la la la, With a fal la la la, With a fal la
With a fal la
(Strict time.)
la, with a fal la la la la la la la la la la, with a
la la la la la la la la la la la la la la la la la la la
la la la la la la la la la la la la la la la la la la la
la la la la la la

SO.
HON.
TOM.
AL.
fal la la la la la la la, With a fal la la la la la
la la la la la la la la la la la la la la la la la la
la la la la la la la la la la la la la la la
(attacca)
With a fal la la la
f
la la la la la la la la la la la
la la la la la la la
f
With a fal la la, With a fal la la, With a fal la
la, With a fal la la la la la la la la la la la la la la la la la la

Allargando.
SO.
la, O Love Love,
HON.
la la la la la la la la la, Love Love,
TOM.
la la la la la la la la, O Love Love,
AL.
la, O Love Love Love,
f Allargando.
G a tempo
molto rit.
Love must e'en break hearts to get a Store of bro - ken hearts to
a tempo
molto rit.

SO.
HON.
TOM.
AL.
pp a tempo
mend. With a fal la la la, With a fal la la la la la la la la la
mend. With a fal la la la, With a fal la la la la la la
mend. With a fal la la la, With a fal la la la la la la
mend, to mend,
rall. molto
rall.
la la la la la la la la la.
la la la la la.
to mend.
rit.
ppp
FL. CL.
Ped.

Nº 8. FINALE.– ACT I.

Cue. SOPHIA:–"I love you."

TOM.

say my love, O say my love Con-fid-ing-ly, Ah! whis-per them once a-

HORN SUST.

BASSOON.

accel.
poco - -
SO.
heart shall e'er be true I love you so, And on - ly know I
accel.
- a - - poco accel.
B
live a - lone for you. I live a - lone for
HORN.
accel.
Allegro. ♩.=80.
f
you I love you so, And
f Allegro.
sf
rit.
on - ly know I live a - lone for
rit.
CL.

Andante con moto.
a tempo primo
SO.
you
My heart, my
TOM.
For aye, my love! For aye, my love! A - bid - ing - ly Those
(Beat quick 6.)
Andante con moto.
(Beat 2.)
p STGS. CL.
SO.
heart shall e'er be true, shall e'er
TOM.
lit - tle words shall live in my heart; And all life long, Like a
SO.
be true.
I'll
TOM
glad sweet song, Bring hap - pi - ness when we're a - part

SO.
say my love, I'll say my love, Con - fid-ing-ly A - gain and oft a -
TOM.
O whis - per them once a - gain O
HORN SUS.
BASSOON.
SO.
f
- gain The words that my breast Holds sweet-est and best And a
TOM.
f
once a - gain And deep in my breast O
f
C
accel. poco a - poco
Allegro.
f
SO.
se - cret they shall re - main. I love
TOM.
f
dear - est and best. They a se - cret shall re - main,
Allegro.
accel. poco - a - poco
f
STGS.
WOOD.
HORNS.

SO.
I love you so, And
TOM.
I love you so, And
rit.
SO.
on - ly know I live a - lone for
TOM.
on - ly know I live a - lone for
rit.
D
SO.
you.
TOM.
you. A cav-a-lier re-quest sir! Pray ex-
BLIFIL. Recit.
Re-lease that la-dy's hand!
TUTTI.
STGS.

SO.
TOM.
-plain.
BLI.
a tempo
'Tis no re-quest I prof-fer; I com - mand!
Allegro.
TUTTI.
f
rit.
f
Allegro agitato. ♩=88.
So! then I re- - main.
With-draw you, Mad-am!
STGS.
sf
rit.
(To Sophia.)
Since you're so lost to sense of shame That all the laws of mod-es-ty you
BASSOON WITH VOICE.

BLI.
flout, To lis-ten to this dog, Whose ve-ry name Was
TRUMPET.
f
p
E
(Chorus enter gradually at back.)
thrown him like a bone, Then hear me out! If't be your fan-cy
TRUMPET.
f
p HORN SUS.
to af-fect The ways of shame-less dames of fash-ion, It does be-hove me to pro-
sf
-tect You from a base-born scoundrel's pas-sion. Aye,
TOM.
TOM. f
You call me scoun-drel!
cresc.
sf
molto
sf
BRASS.

ff
accel.
poco
BLI.
scoun - drel!
(Tom knocks Blifil down. Sophia falls in Tom's arms.)
TOM.
Brute!
sf
accel. - molto
poco
a
poco
F
Allegro agitato. ♩=108.
ff
Ah!
CHO.
Here's a broil!
ff
Ah!
Here's a broil!
Allegro agitato. ♩=108.
TUTTI.
a
poco
sf
CHO.
Here's a broil!
What a coil, O what a coil!
Here's a broil!
What a coil, O what a coil!

CHO.
Ter-ri-ble! Ter-ri-ble! Why this tur-moil?
Ter-ri-ble! Ter-ri-ble! Why this tur-moil?
Ah!
Ah!
What a coil! What a shock-ing thing to quar-rel, And the neigh-bour-
Ah!
Ah!
What a coil! What a shock-ing thing to quar-rel, And the neigh-bour-
ff
G
-hood em-broil! Leav-ing out the ques-tion mor-al, Why this tur-moil?
Ah!
-hood em-broil! Leav-ing out the ques-tion mor-al, Why this tur-moil?
sf
cresc.

Here's a broil,
What a coil!
Here's a broil, here's a broil, here's a
CHO.
What a coil!
Here's a broil,
broil, here's a broil, here's a broil What a coil!
What a coil!
H
what a coil! what a coil!
what a coil! what a coil!
Broader.
Andante.
molto rall.

I
Moderato con espress
SOPHIA.
p
a tempo
He saved my life dear fa - ther, more to him you owe Than
CL. HORN SUS.
pp
CELLI PIZZ.
SO.
grat - i - tude in words a - lone for ev - er can be - stow,
SO.
At your feet be-hold me kneel-ing and ap-peal - ing;
SO.
Let us not be part - ed, for I love him so.

SO.
CHO.
He saved her life, re-mem-ber more to him you owe Than
owe Than gra-ti-
He saved her life, re-mem-ber more to him you owe Than
owe Than gra-ti-
pp
SO.
CHO.
gra-ti-tude in words a-lone for ev-er can be-stow.
-tude by words a-lone for ev-er can be-stow.
gra-ti-tude in words a-lone for ev-er can be-stow. At your
-tude in words, words a-lone for ev-er can be-stow.

SO.
At your feet be-hold me kneel-ing and ap-peal-ing;
At your feet be-hold her kneel-ing and ap-peal-ing;
At your feet be-hold her kneel-ing;
CHO.
feet be-hold her kneel-ing ap-peal-ing;
SO.
Let us not be part-ed, for I love him so.
Let them not be part-ed.
CHO.
Let them not be part-ed.

J
SO.
a tempo
rit.
O part us not, I love him so! O let us not be part-ed,
CHO.
O part them not, she loves him so! she
O part them not, she loves him so! she
STGS. PIZZ.
for I love him so.
Allegro agitato. ♩=144.
WESTERN. (to Tom)
She loves you?
loves, she loves him so.
loves, she loves him so.
ARCO
CL.
WES.
She, my daughter! Do you know Sir, Who and what you are?
STGS.
STGS. FL.
S. DRUM.

K
Allegro. 𝅗𝅥=88.
Risoluto.
WES.
TOM.
I make you no a-
TRUMPET.
OB. HORN SUS.
cresc.
sf
rall.
p STGS. (beat quick 4.)
-pol-o-gies; Love laughs at Her-ald's col-le-ges. Plain
hearts suf-fice For his de-vice, And wise-ly he ac-knowledges
SOP. & CON. in unison.
No Bar Sin-is-ter. He asks but the vi-ci-ni-ty Of
CL. FAG. SUS.

SOP. & CON.
cres - -
hearts that seek af - fin - i - ty, And leaves the oath Of

SOP. & CON.
- - - cen - - - do
mar - riage troth For a Doc - tor of Di - vin - i - ty

SOP. & CON.
TOM.
L
To ad - min - is - ter. And that is my po -
OB.
p

TOM.
- si - tion, Sir; Though low - ly my con - di - tion, Sir, I

TOM.
love this maid, And her to wed Do crave your kind per - mission, Sir.
I love this maid, And her to wed Do crave your kind per - mission Sir.
CHO.
He craves your kind per - mission, Sir.
He craves your kind per - mission, Sir.
f
BRASS.
STGS. HORN.
p
SO.
Ah!
M
a tempo
rall.
mf
And that is his pos -
And that is his pos -
FL. (in triplets)
a tempo
TRIANGLE.

SO.
— And that is his pos - i-tion Sir, I love him so and

TOM.

CHO.
- i-tion Sir. Though low - ly his con - di-tion, Sir, He loves this maid And
- i - tion Sir. Though low - ly his con - di - tion, Sir, He loves this maid And

N appassionato

SO.
on - ly know I live ______ for him, I live for

TOM.

CHO.
crave ______
her to wed Does crave y'r kind per - mis - sion your kind per - mis - sion Sir.
crave ______
her to wed Does crave your kind per - mis - sion Sir.

Broader.
SO.
him for him for aye
TOM.
CHO.
Broader.
ff
BRASS.
Allargando.
rall.
molto rall.
p
I live for him a-lone a-lone for
ff
p
I love her so, and on-ly know I live a-lone for
Allargando.
STGS.
rall.
p molto rall. pp
Ped.

O
SO.
him!
TOM.
her!
ALWORTHY.
ff Recit.
a tempo
ALW.
In-so-lent! This cli-max of in-i-qui-ty all bonds doth sev-er,
Recit.
sf BRASS.
a tempo
ALW.
accel.
I'll suf-fer you no lon-ger! I cast you off for ev-er! I
ALW.
cast you off for ev-er!
Recit.
WESTERN. (to SOPHIA.)
Be-gone un-grate-ful hus-sy! Quit my
sf Recit.

Allegro.
a tempo
cresc.
sempre
WES.
sight!
Quit my sight!
Quit my
CHO.
Shame up - on you!
Shame up - on you! Shame
Shame up - on you!
Shame up - on you! Shame
BRASS.
P
Andante con moto.
Grandioso.
rall.
molto
SO.
For
TOM.
For
WES.
sight!
my
sight.
SOP.
Shame
up - on
you! For
CONT.
Dis-
Shame
up - on
you! Dis-
TUTTI.
(beat quick 6.)

(with animation but not too fast)
SO.
aye, my love, for aye, my love, A - bid - ing - ly, And
TOM.
aye, my love, for aye, my love, A - bid - ing - ly, And
(with animation but too fast)
SOP.
ev - er love, for ev - er love, A - bid - ing - ly, A -
CHO.
CONT.
- cre - tion ov - - er - rides ro - man - ces.
- cre - tion ov - - er - rides ro - man - ces.
(beat moderate 2.)
(with animation but not too fast)
SO.
ev - er, hope shall dwell in my heart, my heart
TOM.
ev - er, hope shall dwell in my heart, And all life long, Like a
- wak-ens hope in ev - 'ry heart, And all life long, Like a
CHO.
And, in spite of sor - row - ing glan - ces, With the pre - sent
And, in spite of sor - row - ing glan - ces, With the pre - sent

SO.
Bring hap-pi-ness when we're a-part, So
TOM.
sad sweet song, Bring hap-pi-ness when we're a-part,
SOP.
sad sweet song, Bring hap-pi-ness to those a-part, The
CONT.
CHO.
cir-cum-stan-ces They must both com-ply.
cir-cum-stan-ces They must both com-ply, must com-ply.
say my love That
That
way of love, the way of love, Be-tid-ing-ly May
Pain-ful 'tis young hearts to sev-er
Pain-ful 'tis young hearts to sev-er

Q
SO.
nothing shall break the tie That has bound us so fast, And shall
TOM.
nothing shall break the tie That has bound us so fast, And shall
SOP.
seem to be all a - wry, But, brave to the last, Be not
CONT.
CHO.
E'en, may be, for ever and ever; See how brave ly
See how
E'en, may be, for ev - er and ev - er; See how brave - ly
f
accel. - - - poco - - - a
SO.
hold to the last, As you bid me say good -
TOM.
hold to the last, As you bid me say good -
accel. - - - poco - - - a
sad or down-cast, Tho' you say good - -
CHO.
they en-deav-our to say good - bye, good - -
brave - ly they en - deav-our to say good - bye, to say good -
they en-deav - our to say good - -
accel. - - - poco - - - a
STGS. FL.

Allegro. ♩. = 88.
SO.
TOM.
CHO.
SOP.
CONT.
poco
-bye, For aye, I
-bye, I
-bye, Al - tho' Al -
-bye, Al - tho', Al - tho' Al -
-bye, Al - tho', Al - tho' Al -
Allegro. ♩. = 88.
TUTTI.
sf
R Animato.
love you so, and on - ly know I live for
love you so, and on - ly know I live for
-tho' you now must say good - bye, Be brave to the last, Be
-tho' you now must say good - bye, Be brave to the last, Be
-tho' you now must say good - bye, Be brave to the last, Be
ff
Animato.
STGS. BRASS.

♩.=138.
SO.
you for aye!
TOM.
you for aye! I
SOP.
brave to the last, Be brave
CONT.
brave to the last, Be brave
TEN.
ff
brave to the last, Be brave be brave
brave be brave, Al -
BASS.
brave to the last, Be brave
accel molto
SO.
TOM.
love you so, and on - ly know I live a - lone
Be brave
Al - tho' you say, you say
CHO.
Al - tho' you say, you say
- tho' you say, Al - tho' you say, you say
brave brave
accel molto
sf

S
SO.
TOM.
for you!
Be brave to the last, Be brave to the last, Be
good - bye, Be brave to the last, Be brave to the last, Be
CHO.
good - bye,
good - bye, Be brave to the last, Be brave to the last, Be
brave, Be brave to the last, Be brave to the last, Be
TUTTI.
SO.
for aye! for aye!
TOM.
for aye! for aye!
brave Be brave Be brave
brave Be brave Be brave
CHO.
brave Be brave Be brave
brave Be brave Be brave
8
Ped.

T Allegro. ♩.=100.
SO.
for aye!
TOM.
for aye!
CHO.
Be brave.
Be brave.
Be brave.
Be brave.
T Allegro. ♩.=100.
8
ff

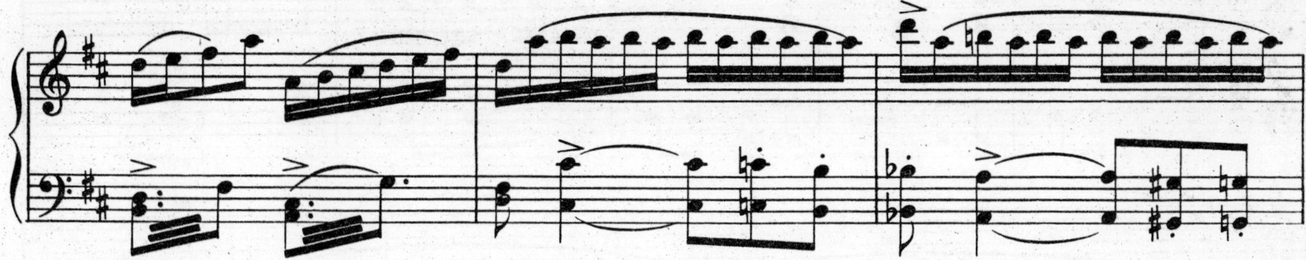

accel.

sf
sf
sf
sf
sf
sf
sff

END OF ACT I.

Act II.

No 9. OPENING CHORUS.

(With Solos for Hostess and Officer.)

B
CHO.
mf
Hur - ry, bus - tle, Hur - ry, bus - tle, Sarv - ing - men and_ wen - ches,
Hur - ry, bus - tle, Hur - ry, bus - tle, Sarv - ing - men and_ wen - ches,
STGS.

C
CHO.
Serv - ing - men and wen - ches, House is full of
Ah
p
Clear a - way the pew - ter pots, Pol - ish up the - ben - ches, The
WOOD WIND.
CHO.
gen - tle - folk, Sta - ble full of coach - es; Hur - ry bus - tle, hur - ry bus - tle
house is full, is full. Hur - ry bus - tle, hur - ry bus - tle
CHO.
Qual - i - ty ap - proach - es.
f
Qual - i - ty ap - proach - es. Bus - tle, hur - ry, bus - tle, Qual - i - ty ap - proach - es,
f
TIMP.

D
p
CHO.
Hur-ry, bus-tle hur-ry, bus-tle, Sarv-ing-men and_ wen-ches, Sarv-
p
Hur-ry, Hur-ry, Sarv-ing-men and wen-ches, Clear a-way the
p BRASS
CHO.
-ing men and wen-ches, House is full of gen-tle folk,
pew-ter pots, Pol-ish up the_ ben-ches, House is full,
E
f
CHO.
Sta-ble full of coach-es; Hur-ry, bus-tle, hur-ry,
f
House is full, is full. Hur-ry, bus-tle,
FL.
f

CHO.

Hur - ry, bus - tle, hur - ry, Hur - ry, bus - tle, hur - ry, bus - tle,

Hur - ry, Hur - ry, bus - tle, hur - ry, bus - tle, hur - ry, bus - tle,

CHO.

hur - ry, bus - tle, bus - tle, bus - tle, Qual - i - ty, Qual - i - ty a - proach -

hur - ry, bus - tle, bus - tle, bus - tle, Qual - i - ty, Qual - i - ty a - proach -

F

CHO.

- - es.

- - es.

STGS. WOOD.

animato

sf *accel. molto*

(Risoluto.)
Recit.
Moderato. ♪ = 152.
a tempo
HOS.
De-sist! I am no fool-ish maid, Who thinks that ev - 'ry i - dle
STGS. CL. SUS.
sf Recit.
p (Beat quick 4)
var - let Is an A - don - is, Be-cause he's paid To swag-ger in a
coat, a coat of scar - let. Rank trea - son! Come, a reb - el here we've
animato
OFFICER.
fp
BRASS.
G
OF.
found; She shall pay for her of - fence in fla - gons round, shall
CHO.
She shall
She shall

OF.
CHO.
pay for her of-fence in fla-gons round; And in her own good
pay for her of-fence in fla-gons round.
pay for her of-fence in fla-gons round.
(broader.)
ale The King's health drink!
The King! the King! the
The King! the King! the
(broader.)
f
H
Allegro marziale. ♪= 168.
1.We
King!
King!
(Beat quick 4)
f
TUTTI.

FULL CHORUS.
OFFICER.
OF.
red-coat sol-diers serve the King, To the tow, row, row, of noi-sy drum and fife. It
Cu-pid leads us to the fray, To the tow, row, row, of noi-sy drum and fife. And
CHO.
To the tow, row, row, of noi-sy drum and fife.
well marked.
S. DRUM.
p (Beat 2) STGS. BRASS.
FULL CHORUS.
sets the maids a-ca-per-ing, So who shall blame us if we cling To the
scat-t'ring ter-ror and dis-may O'er rus-tic ranks in hod-den grey, With a
To the
With a
I
OFFICER.
tow, row, row, To the tow, row, row, In— love as well as strife. No
tow, row, row, With a tow, row, row, We— cap-ture wench and wife. When
tow, row, row, To the tow, row, row, In— love as well as strife.
tow, row, row, With a tow, row, row, We— cap-ture wench and wife.
CL.

OF.
cooing ditties, do we sing, Or sigh, or so demean us; Old Mars he made Olympus ring With a tow, row, row, a tow, row, row, When he went a-courting Venus.
wit and wine have won the day, We leave them sad and sorry, And shoulder arms, and march away With a tow, row, row, a tow, row, row, For a distant field of glory.
CHO.
STGS. CL.
1.
2. Dan
1. Tow, row, row, row, row, row, When he went a-court-ing Ve-nus.
2. Tow, row, row, row, row, row, For a
ENCORE.
TUTTI.
STGS. WOOD.

OF.
CHO.
accel.
dis - tant field, a dis - tant field, a dis - tant field of
PIZZ.
To a dis - tant field of glo - - ry,
glo - ry, To a dis - tant field of glo - - ry, of
TUTTI.
ff
glo - - ry, of glo - ry.
TRUMPET.
PIZZ.
sf
TUTTI.

No 10. SONG.—(Partridge) and CHORUS.

Cue. PARTRIDGE:– "My modest, but unrivalled gifts speak, I think, for themselves."

A
PAR.
Doc-tor, Ad-vis-er, and Bar-ber as well.
Draw you a tooth, or a boil, or a will.
CHO.
Bar-ber as
Boil, or a
Ah!
Ah!
p HORN SUS.
PAR.
CHO.
well, Bar-ber as well, Doc-tor, Ad-vi-ser, and Bar-ber as well.
will, Boil, or a will, Draw you a tooth, or a boil, or a will.
Bar-ber as well Bar-ber as well Bar - - ber as well.
Boil, or a will, Boil, or a will, Boil, or a will.
PAR.
Come and I'll shave you, and if you are ill, Blis-ter and bleed you, and throw in a pill;
Cau-dle a ba-by, or pow-der a wig; Wa-ter di-vine by the turn of a twig;
CHO.
BRASS.
sf
pp
PIZZ.

PAR.
Bring you back cheap from the edge of the grave; The clos - er you're fist - ed, the
Dance a down - der - ry, or drone you a hymn; Set you a rid - dle, or

CHO.

B

PAR.
clos - er the shave.
set you a limb.
Ah
Ah

CHO.
Bring you back cheap from the edge of the grave; The
Dance a down - der - ry, or drone you a hymn;
Bring you back cheap from the edge of the grave; The
Dance a down - der - ry or drone you a hymn;

ARCO.
S. DRUM.

PAR.

CHO.
clos - er you're fist - ed, the clos - er the shave. The clos - er you're fist - ed, the
Set you a rid - dle, or set you a limb. Set you a rid - dle, or
clos - er you're fist - ed, the clos - er the shave. The clos - er you're fist - ed the
Set you a rid - dle, or set you a limb. Set you a rid - dle, or

PAR.
CHO.
rit.
O
clos - er the shave.
set you a limb.
clos - er the shave.
set you a limb.
OB. CL.
rit.
C
a tempo
Ben - ja - min Par - tridge, a Quack if you will, Scho - lar, and mar - vel of
FAG. WITH VOICE.
a tempo
p ten.
sur - gi - cal skill, Lath - er and lan - cet, Per - ru - qui - er, Leech

PAR.

Om - ni - um gath - er - um, Om - ni - um gath - er - um, Om - ni - um gath - er - um, —

CHO.

PAR.

— Some-thing of each.

1.

CHO.

f

Yes, some-thing of each, some-thing of each,

f

Yes, some-thing of each, some-thing of each,

f

TUTTI.

PAR.

Last time.

each.

CHO.

Yes, some-thing of each.

sf

Ah! —

Yes some-thing of each.

STGS.

PICC. FL.

D.S.

PAR.
CHO.
Ben-ja-min Par-tridge, a Quack if you will, Scho-lar and mar-vel of
mf
Ben-ja-min Par-tridge, a Quack if you will, Scho-lar and mar-vel of
sur-gi-cal skill, Lath-er and lan-cet, Per-ru-qui-er, Leech;
sf
Ah!
sur-gi-cal skill, Lath-er and lan-cet, Per-ru-qui-er, Leech;
Om-ni-um gath-er-um, Om-ni-um gath-er-um, Om-ni-um gath-er-um,
Om-ni-um gath-er-um, Om-ni-um gath-er-um, Om-ni-um gath-er-um,
Om-ni-um gath-er-um, Om-ni-um gath-er-um, Om-ni-um gath-er-um,

Animato.
PAR.
Some-thing of each.
Om-ni-um gath-er-um,
CHO.
Some-thing of each.
Om-ni-um gath-er-um,
Some-thing of each.
Om-ni-um gath-er-um,
Animato.
f
BRASS.
PAR.
Om-ni-um gath-er-um, some-thing of
CHO.
Om-ni-um gath-er-um, some-thing of
Om-ni-um gath-er-um, some-thing of
PAR.
each.
CHO.
each.
each.
accel.
ENCORE.
Segue Dance.

DANCE.

Allegro moderato. ♩.=96.

(*Not too fast.*)

E
STGS. WOOD.
rit.
a tempo
pp

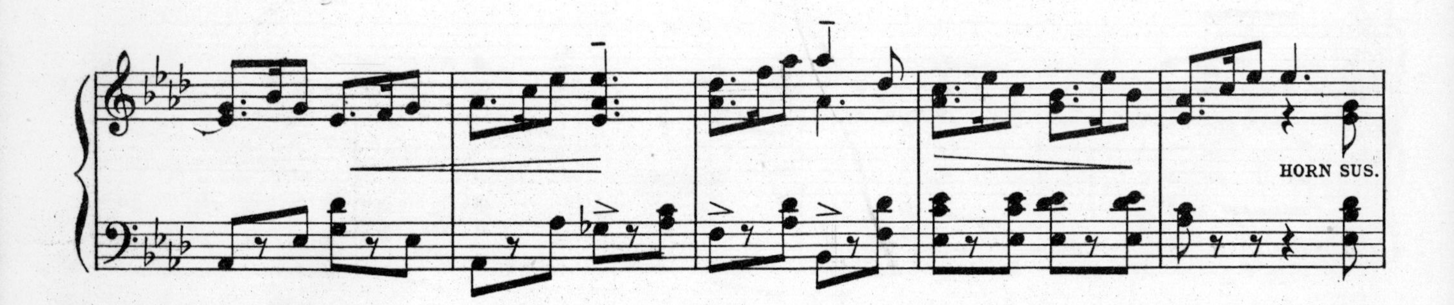
HORN SUS.

accel
al
fine.

FL. CL.
sf
PIZZ.
sf
sf

No. 11. SONG- (Sophia.)

"DREAM O' DAY JILL."

Cue. SOPHIA:- "like a Dream o' Day Jill."

A Animato.
SO.
gen - tle - man great Of no - ble es - tate— At the
(Beat 2.)
BRASS.
SO.
church on the hill" Said Dream o' Day Jill! Heigh - ho! Heigh -
Broader.
f
f
Ped.
*
SO.
- ho! "For no - bo - dy less shall mar - ry me" It's
p
rall.
p
colla voce.
rall.
Ped.
*
B a tempo giocoso.
SO.
hey dil - ly, dil - ly, dil - ly, call the ducks from the pond, There are
STGS. WOOD HORN.
p
TRI.
(Beat quick 3.)
PIZZ.

SO.
cows to be milk'd in the mea - dow be - yond: There are

cresc.
SO.
eggs to take to mar - ket, and grist to the mill, And
cresc.

p delicato.
SO.
f
who'll make a pret - ty la - dy, la - dy, pret - ty la - dy, And
f
PIZZ.
p delicato.

rit.
SO.
who'll make a pret - ty la - dy Of Dream o' Day
ARCO.
colla voce
rit.

ENCORE.
a tempo
SO.
Jill?
mf TUTTI.
a tempo
(Beat quick 6.)

SO.
rit.
All in her
colla voce

a tempo.
SO.
pet - ti - coat of mus - a - lin Goes Dream o' Day Jill, And her
p STGS.

SO.
own pret - ty feet they car - ry her To the church on the hill, Where
FL.

SO.
some - bo - dy, some - bo - dy waits to mar - ry her; And
sf
A (2nd Verse.)
Animato.
poor tho' he be, right glad - ly goes she, For "yes" with a will said
p
BRASS.
Broader.
f
p
Dream o' Day Jill, Heigh - ho! Heigh - ho! To the
f
p
Ped. * Ped. *
rall.
first one who came to mar - ry her. It's
colla voce
rall.

B (2nd Verse.)
a tempo giocoso.
SO.
hey dil - ly, dil - ly, dil - ly, call the ducks from the pond, There are
STGS. WOOD HORNS.
p
TRI.
PIZZ.
cows to be milk'd in the mea - dow be - yond; But she's
cresc.
brought her eggs to mar - ket, as wise maid - ens will Who
f
p delicato.
sigh to be pret - ty la - dies, la - dies, pret - ty la - dies, Who
PIZZ.
p delicato

SO.
sigh to be pret - ty la - - - - dies Like Dream o' Day
accel.
ARCO.
accel.
STGS. WOOD.
SO.
Jill, Like Dream o' Day Jill, Ah!
f
Meno mosso.
a tempo.
SO.
Who sigh to be pret - ty la - dies Like Dream o' Day
TUTTI.
f
Meno mosso.
STGS.
a tempo.
Ped.
*
BRASS.
SO.
Jill!
Molto allegro.
ff
sf

No. 12. SONG.– (Gregory and CHORUS.)

cue: GREGORY: – "We don't never hurry nor worry where I do come from."

GR.
Maw - ther 'e zaid:—"Whoi 'tis Un - cle Jan Tap - pit a - rose from the dead!"
picked up vur dead, But by mar - ci - ful prov - i - dence vell on 'is 'ead.
vind - in' a 'are W'aat 'ad some 'ow or o - ther got catch'd in a snare.
touch'd 'im zo zore, That they thought as e'd zmile a - gin niv - ver no more.
CHO.
f Animato
Wi 'is
f Animato
Wi 'is
FL.
f
GR.
CHO.
Hee! Dob - bin! Ho! Dob - bin! Gee! Dob - bin! Whoa! Dob - bin! Zum-mer - zet med - ders vur
Hee! Dob - bin! Ho! Dob - bin! Gee! Dob - bin! Whoa! Dob - bin! Zum-mer - zet med - ders vur
BRASS.

A
GR.
Zeys my Vey - ther to Maw - ther, "Just luk at 'is nose! 'E
An' my school-mais - ter zaid:-"Waarm your breech - es oi wull! Vur oi
But when oi went a zeek - in' ov mush - rooms, vur sure, They did
When a wag - gon ran ov - ver my vace, an' oi laid All a-
CHO.
clov - ver.
clov - ver.
STGS. FAG. SUS.
pp
GR.
nub - but wants snuff col - oured breech - es an' 'ose;"
caan't get no larn - in' in - soide ov your skull;"
gaol me vur poach - in' an zquire 'e zwore:
zwound - in', they zaid:-"'E's been jilt - ing a maid;"
"Odd
CHO.
FL. CL.
sf
Ped.
*

GR.

drat 'ee! An' 'ang 'ee! Luk at 'ee! whoi dang 'ee! 'E's Un-cle Jan Tap-pit all

CHO.

f. *p*

1st, 2nd & 3rd time.

GR.

ov - ver.

CHO.

E's Un - cle Jan Tap-pit, 'E's Un - cle Jan

E's Un - cle Jan Tap-pit, 'E's Un - cle Jan

TUTTI. *sf* *sf*

Last time.

GR.

2. Gurt ov - ver
3. Gurt
4. Gurt

CHO.

Tap-pit all ov-ver. Odd

Tap-pit all ov-ver. Odd

sf

D.S.

GR.
CHO.
drat 'ee! An 'ang 'ee! Luk at 'ee whoi dang 'ee! 'E's Un - cle Jan Tap - pit all
drat 'ee! An 'ang 'ee! Luk at 'ee whoi dang 'ee! 'E's Un - cle Jan Tap - pit all
B
ov - ver, all ov - ver, all ov - - - ver.
ov - ver, all ov - ver, all ov - - - ver.
sf
accel.
sf

No. 12½.

JIG.

Presto. ♩.= 178.
STGS.
TAMB.

WOOD HORNS.

JIG.
STGS.

C
PICC. CL.
PIZZ.

D
BRASS.

FL.
BRASS.

OB. SUS.

E

F
BRASS.

GIRLS.
CHO.
With a
MEN.
rit
TUTTI.

G
CHO.
Fal la la la la la la la
Fal la la la la la la la
ff a tempo
la, With a Fal la la la la la la la
la, With a Fal la la la la la la la
K
1.
2.
sf
la, With a la.
la, With a la.
Lunga pausa
(confused noise heard off)
sff
fff
STGS. CYMB.

Molto agitato.
CHORUS. (entering excitedly.)
CHO.
My La - dy's coach has been at - tack'd By high - way - men
My La - dy's coach has been at - tack'd By high - way - men
Molto agitato.
STGS.
TUTTI.
CHORUS. (on stage.)
with pis - tols load - ed And fa - ces blacked! Lawks a - mus - sy!
with pis - tols load - ed And fa - ces blacked! Lawks a - mus - sy!
L
CHORUS. (just entering)
Lawks a mus - sy! Where be? Say! A - down by cop - pice.
Lawks a mus - sy! Where be? Say! A - down by cop - pice.
HORN.
FL. OB. CL.

FULL CHORUS.
rit.
a tempo
A-lack a-day! a-lack a-day!
CHO.
A-lack a-day! a-lack a-day!
TUTTI.
TIMP.
BRASS.
FAG.
HOSTESS.
M
Your noise her La-dy-ship a-larms, She
STGS.
HOS.
swoons in her pre-ser-ver's arms.
So let un bide to-geth-er, Nay,
HORN.

N
p.
— We be not want-ed, then come a-way
come a-
— We be not want-ed, then come a-way, a-way, then come a-
PIZZ.
dim.
-way
pp
-way, come a-way, come a-way, come a-way, Hush! hush! hush! hush! a
-way, come a-way, come a-way, come a-way,
-way, a-way, then come a-way, Hush! hush! hush! hush! a
PIZZ.
TIMP.
ppp
-way, a-way, Hush! hush! hush!
-way, a-way, Hush! hush! hush!
pppp

Nº 13. SONG.-(Honour.)

cue. HONOUR:—"As the barber looks at me."

A
HON.
oh! he look'd at me; He look'd a-skance at me. I
oh! he look'd at me; He look'd a-skance at me. That
FL.
STGS.
pp
TRIANG.
HON.
felt my cheeks go flam-in' red I had-n't got eyes in the back of my head,
he was tall and brave I knew, Tho' ne-ver a glance at him I threw;
B
HON.
But I knew that he look'd, I knew that he look'd, I knew that he look'd at
But I knew that he look'd, I knew that he look'd, I knew that he look'd at
pp
sf
p PIZZ.
dim.
pp
HON.
me, I knew! I knew!
me, I knew! I knew!
pp
ARCO
f
TUTTI.

HON.
2. We
3. Said
OB.
p
STGS. CL.
(3) he: "I'm go-ing to Lon - don town, And I've lost my way a-
(4) when I show'd him the way to go, He light - ly stoop'd to his
-cross the Down If one of you maids will show the way A
sad - dle bow, With "Here's your kiss, and a sil - ver crown, And
BRASS.
STGS.
kiss for the ser - vice I will pay." And
come with me, sweet, to Lon - don town." And
TRUMPET.

HON.
oh! he look'd at me; He look'd a - skance at
oh! he look'd at me; He look'd a - skance at
FL.
STGS.
pp
TRIANG.
HON.
me. So, lest he lost his way a - gain, I
me. But when I found the heart to cry "Kind
HON.
took him as far as the top o' the lane For I
Sir, d'ye see a - ny green in my eye?" Oh! the
HON.
knew that he look'd, I knew that he look'd I knew that he look'd at
way that he look'd, The way that he look'd The way that he look'd at
pp
PIZZ.
dim.
pp

1.
HON.
me. I knew! I knew!
ARCO.

HON.
ENCORE.
TUTTI.

HON.
2.
4. And me The way that he look'd, he
animato

HON.
look'd at me.

No. 14. LAUGHING TRIO.–(Honour, Gregory and Partridge.)

cue. GREGORY:–"Ye-es, I begin to see it now!"

A
HON.
ho! ho! ho! ho! ho! I do ad - mit the point I missed, Till you
ho! ho! ho! ho! ho! I vow no scan - dal doth es - cape Them
GREG.
ho! ho! ho! ho! ho!
ho! ho! ho! ho! ho!
PART.
ho! ho! ho! ho! ho!
ho! ho! ho! ho! ho!
HORN SUS.
pp
STGS. PIZZ.
HON.
f
put me in the vein, And gave the joke a mer - ry, mer - ry twist, That
be it near or far, And while, and while the dul - lards are a - gape I
GREG.
PART.
FL. WITH VOICE.
f
p

HON.
made it all as plain as plain.
catch the joke and there you are.
Ha
GREG.
That made it all as plain as plain.
I catch the joke and there you are.
PART.
That made it all as plain as plain.
I catch the joke and there you are.
HON.
ha ha ha! Ha ha ha ha ha ha ha ha
GREG.
Ha ha ha ha! ha ha ha ha ha ha ha
PART.
Ha ha ha ha! ha ha ha ha ha ha ha
HON.
ha! Then
GREG.
ha! Ho ho ho ho ho ho ho!
PART.
ha! Ho ho ho ho ho ho ho!

B
leggiero
HON.
GREG.
PART.
Let's be mer-ry, mer-ry, mer-ry, mer-ry, mer-ry, mer-ry while we
STGS.
leggiero
pp
Ped. TRIANG.
may;— 'Tis bet-ter to be blithe and gay,— Than cry the live-long
day, Then come, we'll bu-ry, bu-ry, bu-ry, bu-ry, bu-ry, bu-ry care a-
Then come, we'll bu-ry, bu-ry, bu-ry, bu-ry, bu-ry, bu-ry care a-
Then come, we'll bu ry, bu-ry, bu-ry, bu-ry, bu-ry, bu-ry care a-
sf
p
TUTTI.
STGS.FL.

HON.
GREG.
PART.
way.— Ha ha ha ha! Ha ha ha ha ha ha ha ha
way.— Ho ho ho ho! ho ho! ho ho!
way.— Ho ho ho ho! ho ho! ho ho!
STGS. WOOD. HORNS.
BRASS.
ha ha ha ha! Be mer-ry, mer-ry while — we may. —
ho ho ho ho! Be mer-ry, mer-ry while — we may. —
ho ho ho ho! Be mer-ry, mer-ry while — we may. —
1.
TUTTI.
2. Thy — we — may. —
— we may. —
— we may. —
2.
D
ENCORE.
Allegro molto.
D. S.
TAMB.

23063.

Nº 15. SONG.- (Tom) and CHORUS.

"A SOLDIER'S SCARLET COAT."

cue. TOM:– "Here's to the crimson wine, and the Soldier's scarlet coat."

Words by
H. BESWICK.

A
TOM.
guns are loud-ly crashing.
plaints it calms and hushes.
In fierce at-tack, At siege or sack, The
Its bou-quet rare Be-yond com-pare, Gives
FL.PICC.
f
p
BRASS.
Ped.
*
p rit. a tempo
scarlet coat is ev-er lead-ing; Be-fore its hue Fall maid-ens too, In spite of all their
pleasure to the thirst-y fel-low; Ripe wine and old Is more than gold, And makes a man both
p rit. a tempo
HORNS.
B Animato.
ff
pret-ty, pret-ty, plead-ing.
wise and mel-low.
Then
CHO.
f
Then sing!
Then
ff
Then sing!
Then
Animato.
f
BRASS.

TOM.
sing Old Rose, and let the bel-lows burn, Ah!

CHO.
sing Old Rose, and let the bel-lows {burn, For som-bre liv-'ries / burn, For pale po-ta-tions}

sing Old Rose, and let, and let the bel-lows {burn, For som-bre liv - 'ries / burn, For pale po - ta - tions}

ff

p

(C)

TOM.
Lust-y lads! Lust-y lads!

CHO.
much I spurn Scar-let bright is the tint for me, / much I spurn Crim-son wine is the wine for me, Lust-y lads!

much I spurn Scar-let bright is the tint for me, / much I spurn Crim-son wine is the wine for me, Lust-y lads!

f

sf *sf* *sf*

TUTTI.

TOM.
CHO.
Lads of the West! Lust - y Lads of the West Coun - tree, Of the
West!
Lads of the West! O Lust - y Lads of the West Coun - tree, Of the
Lads of the West! O Lust - y Lads of the West Coun - tree, Of the
sf
Ped.
1.
mer - ry, mer - ry West Coun - tree!
STGS. CL.
f
mf
2. Red
2.
- tree!
of the West,
- tree! of the
- tree! of the

TOM.
The lads of the West, the West
of the West
CHO.
West, of the West, The lads of the West, the West
West, of the West, The lads of the West, the West
TOM.
Coun - tree!
CHO.
Coun - tree!
Coun - tree!

Nº 16. SONG—(Sophia) and CHORUS.

cue: SOPHIA:—"All is lost! And he was all the world to me."

SOPH.
hey der-ry down, with a der-ry down) As he tend-eth, he tend-eth it
rit.
pp
all day long! (With a hey der-ry down, with a
A a tempo
der-ry down.)
Hey der-ry down,
CHO.
Hey der-ry down a!
Hey der-ry down a!
OB. WITH VOICE.
ENCORE.
a tempo
mf
But one day the gar-den a cold wind sears; (With a
SOLO LEADER.
pp
Ped.
*

SOPH.
hey der-ry down, with a der-ry down) In vain you wa-ter it
CHO.
ppp
Hey der-ry down a der-ry down a
Hey der-ry down a der-ry down a
Ped. * Ped. * (simile)
SOPH.
with your tears; (With a hey der-ry down, with a
CHO.
ppp
Hey der-ry
Hey der-ry
SOPH.
der-ry down) Ev-'ry blos-som, it droop-eth its head (With a
CHO.
down a! der-ry down a!
down a! der-ry down a!
CL. HORN.
TIMP.

SOPH.
hey der-ry down, with a der-ry down) All are with-er'd, are with-er'd, and
CHO.
ppp
Hey der-ry down a der-ry down a
Hey der-ry down a der-ry down a
rit.
Love is dead. (With a hey der-ry down, with a der-ry down.
a tempo
Hey der-ry
mf
OB. WITH VOICE.
rit.
a tempo
mf
rit.
pp
Hey der-ry down!
down, Hey der-ry down-a, der-ry down, der-ry down!
Hey der-ry down-a, der-ry down, der-ry down!
rit.
pp
ppp
B
Exit SOPHIA.
mf OB.
con espress.
p
pp
Ped.
*

Nº 17. FINALE - ACT II.

cue. BLIFIL:– "Squire! Squire! Your daughter is found."

Allegro molto agitato. ♩=152.

TOM.
TOM.
WESTERN.
p
f
Squire Wes-tern!
Tom Jones!
(Now I've caught her!) I
STGS
p
f
WEST.
TOM.
want my daugh-ter.
I have not seen her.
cresc.
BRASS
D
WESTERN.
WEST.
f
Come! she is in here. Come!
f
TUTTI.
Presto.
WEST.
sf
(Enter Lady Bellaston from room.)
E
F
Moderato.
SOPRANOS & CONTRALTOS.
WEST.
f
Ha!
STGS WOOD
sf
TUTTI.

Allegretto. ♩.= 112.
Giocoso. (mockingly)
CHO.
Ha Ha ha ha ho ho ho ho! A ve - ry fine im-brog - li - o! "The
clue I hold," and ov - er rolled, Sir An - to-ny, An - to - ny Row - ley O!
clue I hold," and ov - er rolled, Sir An - to-ny, An - to - ny Row - ley. Hey
Ah!
ho! Sir An - to - ny Row - ley O!
Ha ha ha ha ho
ho ho ho! A ve - ry fine im - brog - li - o! "The

G
CHO.
clue I hold," And ov - er rolled Sir An - to - ny, An - to - ny,
clue I hold," And ov - er rolled Sir An - to - ny, An - to - ny,
STGS. BRASS.
An - to - ny, An - to - ny, An - to - ny Row - - ley O!
An - to - ny, An - to - ny, An - to - ny Row - - ley O!
sf
accel:
Allegro moderato. 𝅗𝅥 = 64.
LADY B. to TOM.
Lady B.
TRUMPET.
meno mosso molto rall:
I know your se - cret now; You
STGS. FL.
pp
Ped.
Ped.

Lady B.

look for one a - bove — you. O poor, un - hap - py boy, — To

Ped. * Ped. *

Lady B.

be the bro - ken toy — Of one who does not love — you, who

Ped. *

Lady B.

does not love you.

H

TOM. *f*

'Tis false! I vow 'tis false!

Lady B.

Aye, false is she I vow. When

mf

p HORN SUS.

Ped. *

Lady B.

e - vil fate be - tide — you To turn and fly, — Your

VIO I.

Lady B.

pp

love were I, — My place should be be - side you —

rit:

pp

rit:

Ped. * Ped. * Ped. *

J
a tempo (animato)
Lady B.
TOM.
Your love were
Oh! say not so! I know She loves me, tho' Our part - ing may
cantabile
a tempo mf (animato)
STGS. WOOD. HORN.
I. Though
be, per - chance for ev - er, She will for - get me nev - er! Our
e - vil fate be - tide, And all the world de - ride, Still
part - ing be per - chance for ev - er, She will for
I would fly to take my place be - side you, Your own true
get, for - get, me nev - er, My own true

Lady B.
rit.
a tempo
love were I.
TOM.
rit.
a tempo
love is she.
CHO.
UNIS.
mf
The maid-en who Is fond and true, And faith-ful to Her love will
rit.
a tempo
mf
cantabile
BRASS.
CHO.
ev-er stand be-side him, What-ev-er may be-tide him, And
CHO.
with her cheer-ing pres-ence wak-en hope a-new.

K
Lady B.
TOM.
CHO.
mf
Forget, forget You ever met This maid false-hearted, To
pp A - waken hope a-new. The
pp
A-waken hope a-new, a-wak - en hope, a-wak - en
p
pp
Ped.
accel.
turn and fly!
Your love were I,
She loves me still!
She
true,
maid - en who
Is fond and true,
hope.
The maid - en who
is
VIO. I.
p
accel.
mf
Ped.
Ped.

Lady B.
TOM.
CHO.
rit.
My place should be be - side you.
loves me still!
fond and true Will ev - er stand be - side
fond and true Will ev - er stand be - side
TIMP.
Grandioso.
Your own, your own true
She loves, she loves me
him, The maid - en who Is fond and true And faith - ful to Her love, will
him, The maid - en who Is fond and true And faith - ful to Her love, will
Grandioso.
TUTTI.

Lady B.
love, Your own true love were I, Tho'
TOM.
though our part - ing may be for ev - er, Our
CHO.
ev - er stand be - side him, What - ev - er may be - tide him, Will
ev - er stand be - side him, What - ev - er may be - tide him, Will
Lady B.
e - vil fate be - tide, And all the world de - ride. Still
rall. molto
TOM.
part - ing be per - chance for ev - er, She will for -
CHO.
ev - er stand be - side, Though all the world de - ride, And
ev - er stand be - side, Though all the world de - ride, And
rall. molto
Ped. * Ped. *

Allargando.
Lady B.
would I fly To take my place be - side you, Your own true love were
TOM.
- get, for - get me nev - er, My own true love is
CHO.
with her cheer - ing pres - ence wak - en hope, a - wak - en hope a -
cheer - ing pres - ence
with her cheer - ing pres - ence a - wak - en hope a -
rit.
STGS.
Allargando.
Allegro marziale.
I!
she!
- new.
- new.
Allegro marziale. (With great spirit.)
TRUMPET.
S. DRUM.

OFFICER. (to Tom)
L
OF.
A toss — for fic-kle maids! Their coin has not the
p STGS.
sf
pro-per ring; Cry fie! on them for sor-ry sor-ry jades, And be a
sol-dier, a sol-dier of the King.
TOM. (spoken) Aye! that will I!
TOM.
Allegro moderato. ♩=112.
'Tis
STGS.
PICC. FAG.
ff TUTTI. (marcato.)
sf sf
sf p
pp
B.D. CYM.
TOM.
bet-ter to lie in a ditch, I swear, With your wea-zen neat-ly slit, Than
ten.

TOM.
eat your heart out in des-pair For a heart-less jilt Who does not care A
M
TOM.
jot for it.
A jot for it, Who does not care a jot for it!
CHO.
A jot for it, Who does not care a jot for it!
f
BRASS.
TOM.
'Tis bet-ter to love and march a-way, Or
sf
pp
CYM.
TOM.
in a tav-ern sit, And drink good liq-uor all the day, And

N
TOM.
leave a kiss be - hind to pay The shot for it.
TRUMPET.
Alla marcia. (Con spirito.)
Ah! For a sol - dier's life Has
p
STGS CL. HORN.
hon-our and glo - ry a - bound - ing, Shrill - tongued fife And
O
bu - gle for ev - er re - sound - ing.
p
Kiss-me-quick-my-loves in plen - ty,
FL.
leggiero
TRIANG.
OFFICER.
f
Come - ly maids of sweet and twen - ty! Come, come, come, The
f
BRASS.

OF.
sol - dier fol - lows the drum, And the lass - es, the lass - es fol - low the
S. DRUM.
OF.
sol - dier, The lass - es fol - low, fol - low the
life Has
CHO.
For a sol - dier's life Has hon - our and glo - ry a -
For a sol - dier's life Has hon - our and glo - ry a -
TUTTI.
OF.
sol - dier.
CHO.
- bound - ing, Shrill - tongued fife, And bu - gle for ev - er re - sound - ing.
- bound - ing, Shrill - tongued fife, And bu - gle for ev - er re - sound - ing.

P
TOM.
TOM.
Kiss– me-quick-my-loves in plen-ty, Come-ly maids of sweet and twen-ty,
UNIS.
Kiss– me-quick-my-loves in plen-ty, Come-ly maids of sweet and twen-ty,
CHO.
Ah!
Kiss - me - quick - my - loves in plen - ty,
FL.
pp
Come, The sol-dier fol-lows the drum.
Come, come, come, The sol - dier fol - lows the drum.
The
accel. molto
BRASS.
(Tom sees Sophia's muff.)
Recit.
TOM. (to Partridge)
Say, what have you there?
Andante.
HOSTESS. (spoken)
A lady's muff
TUTTI.
STGS.
Andante.
OB.
HORN.
Ped.

Andante.

TOM.

p *dim.*

I seem to know it, Ah! me! — and yet, and yet it

contenerezza.

p Andante.

Ped. * Ped. * Ped. * Ped. * Ped. * Ped. * Ped. * Ped. *

Ⓣ Allegro.

TOM.

rit.

can-not be!

(Suddenly and excitedly.)

The pa-per that is pinned there-on! Whose writ-ing bears it?

Molto Allegro.

Ⓣ STGS.

sf *Recit.*

a tempo *f*

Ped. *

HOSTESS.

TOM.

f

"So-phi-a Western!"

'Tis the young la-dy's who hath late-ly gone a-

sf *sf*

sf *(strict time.)*

Ped.

STGS.

TOM. (to Partridge)

HOST.

-way Fool! Fool! Now am I un-done! Say, where is she?

sf *sf* *sf* *sf* *sf*

f

BRASS.

Allegro agitato.
TOM.
Good
CHO.
She's on the road to London, She's on the road to London.
She's on the road to London, She's on the road to London.
Allegro agitato.
STGS.
PIZZ.
TOM.
horses, quick, Come, let's be-gone!
U
Recit.
a tempo
TOM.
Stay! my purse. Bah! thas nothing in it! Then will I
BRASS.
Allegro.
go a-foot.
STGS. FL.

(to TOM.)
p (aside.)
Lady B.
I must not lose him yet.
mf
You are em - bar - rass'd;
(CL. WITH VOICE.)
pp
p
I am in your debt,
f amoroso
Aye that and deep - ly.
amoroso
WOOD. HORN.
Pray com - mand me.
V Allegro.
I go to Lon - don al - so, And my
FL. CL. WITH VOICE.
f
pp
PIZZ.
coach is at your ser - vice;
Lend me your kind pro - tec - tion.
TOM.
Ah!
VIOL. I.
ff Recit.
TOM.
Ma - dam, How can I thank you?
Come! who knows? my luck may
sf
sf
BRASS.

a tempo
TOM.
turn. If not I'll yet be a soldier.
W Allegro. ♩=112.
CHO.
His luck may turn, his luck may
His luck may turn, his luck may
STGS. HORN.
a tempo
sf
sf
Allegro. ♩=112.
p
TRUMPET. S. DRUM.
cresc.
turn, If not he'll be a sol - dier, a
turn, If not he'll be a sol - dier, a
f
cresc.
BRASS. FAG.
Lady B. & TOM.
rall.
molto
For a
sol - - - dier! For a
sol - - - dier! For a
rall.
molto

Pesante.
ff a tempo
Lady B.
sol - dier's life Has hon - our and glo - ry a - bound - ing,
TOM.
sol - dier's life Has hon - our and glo - ry a - bound - ing,
CHO.
life Has
sol - dier's life Has hon - our and glo - ry a - bound - ing,
sol - dier's life Has hon - our and glo - ry a - bound - ing,
Pesante.
ff a tempo
TUTTI.
Lady B.
Shrill - tongued fife, And bu - gle for ev - er re - sound - ing,
TOM.
Shrill - tongued fife, And bu - gle for ev - er re - sound - ing,
CHO.
Shrill - tongued fife, And bu - gle for ev - er re - sound - ing,
Shrill - tongued fife, And bu - gle for ev - er re - sound - ing,

Lady B.
TOM.
CHO.
p
Ah!
p unis.
Kiss - me - quick - my - loves in plen - ty, Come - ly maids of sweet and twen - ty,
Ah!
Kiss - me - quick - my - loves in plen - ty,
f
Come, The sol - dier fol - lows the drum, And the
Come, come, come, The sol - dier fol - lows the drum, And the

X Animato.
Lady B.
lasses, the lasses follow the sol - - dier. The soldier's
TOM.
lasses, the lasses follow the sol - - dier. The soldier's
CHO.
lasses, the lasses follow the sol - - dier. The sol - dier's
lasses, the lasses follow the sol - - dier. The sol - dier's
Animato.
S. DRUM.
Lady B.
life is one of fame and glo-ry. The soldier's life is praised in
TOM.
life is one of fame and glo-ry. The soldier's life is praised in
CHO.
life is one of fame and glo-ry. The sol - dier's life is
life is one of glo - ry. The sol - dier's life is
sempre staccato.

Lady B.
TOM
CHO.
song and sto-ry, The sol - dier talks of vic - to-
song and sto-ry, The sol - dier talks of vic - to -
praised in song and sto-ry, The sol - dier talks of vic - to-
The sol - dier talks of vic - to-
praised in song and sto - ry, The sol - dier talks of vic - to -
Y
-ry, The din of can-nons' rat-tle, The sound of drum,—
-ry, The din of can-nons'
-ry The din of can-nons' rat-tle, The sound of drum, The din of can-nons'
-ry
-ry, The din of can-nons' rat-tle, The sound of drum, The din of can-nons'
FL.
BRASS WITH VOICE.
VIO.I.

Lady B.
Then, hey! for the life of a sol -
TOM.
rat-tle, the sound of drum. Then, hey! for the life of a sol -
CHO.
rat-tle, the sound of drum. Then, hey! for the life of a sol -
rat-tle, the sound of drum. Then, hey! for the life of a sol -
FL.
Ped.
Più vivo.
-dier! and march, and march a
-dier! and march, and march a -
-dier! and march a - way, and march a - way, a -
-dier! and march a - way, and march a - way, a -
Più vivo.
sf
B.D. & CYM.

Lady B.
-way,
Ah!
accel.
And
TOM.
-way, March a - way, and march a - way, and march a - way, and march a - way,
And
Ah!
accel.
CHO.
-way, March a - way, and march a - way, and march a - way, and march a - way,
And
-way, March a - way, and march a - way, and march a - way, and march a - way,
And
STGS. WOOD. HORNS.
accel.
TRUMPET.
Ped.
Lady B.
ff
march a - way, and march
TOM.
ff
march a - way, and march
CHO.
ff
march a - way, and march
ff
march a - way, and march
BRASS.

Z
Lady B.
a - way.
TOM.
a - way.
CHO.
a - way.
a - way.
TUTTI.
sf
animato
lunga pausa
sf
sf

END OF ACT II.

No. 18.

Act III.

MORRIS DANCE & GAVOTTE.

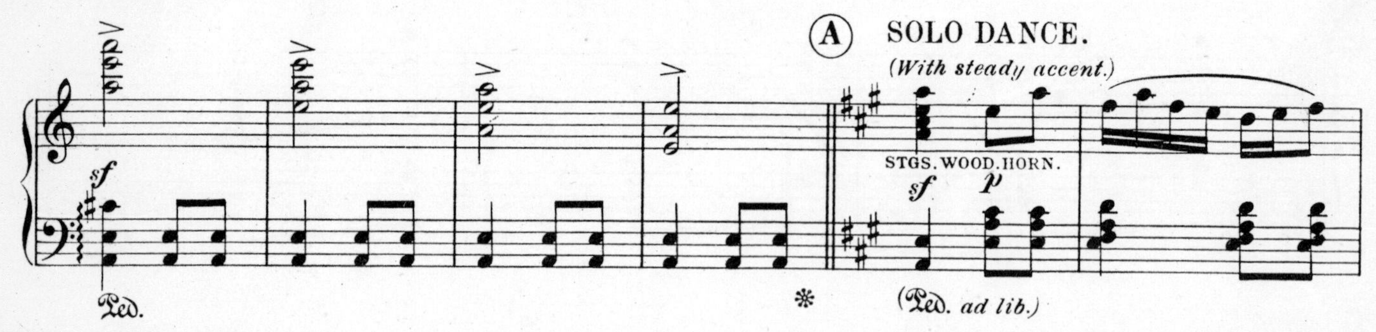

sf
p
sf
p

TRUMPET.

B
sf
TUTTI.

sf

(Repeat 8ve higher.)
VIO.I.OB.
p
PIZZ.

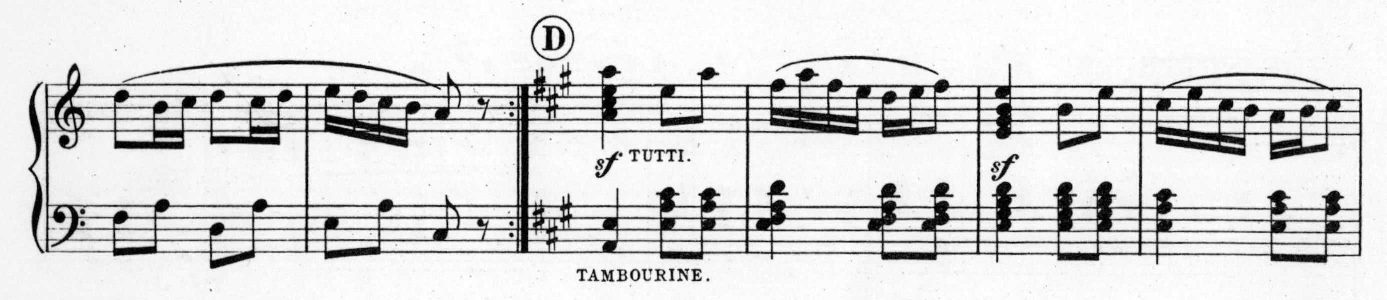

Ped. *

(Exit Principal Dancer.)

♩ = 104.
p
Glass of
p
rall, FL.
p
Ped.
Ped.

GAVOTTE.
fash - ion. Mould of form, Ac - me of e - le-gance, Height of gen - til - i - ty; Mo - dish
(Not too fast.)
STGS. WOOD. HORNS.

p
mf
f
Town and eke Ar - ca - dia, These art thou O Ran - e - lagh. Mark our airs, our con - ver -
p
mf
mf
p
Ped.

p
-sa - tion, Cut of coat and hang of gown; Each of
p
p
them an ed - u - ca - tion In the man - ners of the
of the
pp
F
Town. Glass of fash - ion, Mould of form, Ac - me of
pp
pp

TRIANG.

e - le - gance, Height of gen - til - i - ty; Mo - dish Town and eke Ar -

These art

- ca - dia. These art thou O Ran - e - lagh.

f *p*

ENCORE.

Animato.

sostenuto

CELLI. *f*

Ped.

G
pp
Glass of fash - ion, Mould of
form, Ac - me of e - le-gance, Height of gen - ti - li - ty; Mo-dish
STGS. WOOD. HORN.
PIZZ.
meno mosso
rall.
allargando
rall. molto
Town and eke Ar - ca - dia. Ran - e - lagh! All these art thou!
f STGS.
p

No. 19. SONG. — (Honour) and MALE CHORUS.

cue. HONOUR:— "Men give what they can afford, and take what they can get."

A
HON.
lark sang ti - ra li - ra High up in the air.
dance with me a mea-sure, The fid - dler waits there."
blush - ing, but she gave him Her heart then and there.
pp
CHO
1. And all for a green
2. And all for a green
3. And all for a green
pp
Ah!
FAG.
pp
HON.
And all for a rib - bon To tie in her
And all for a rib - bon She danced at the
And all for a rib - bon He bought at the
rib - bon She walk'd to the Fair.
rib - bon She danced at the Fair.
rib - bon He bought at the Fair.
CHO
mf

HON.
CHO.
a tempo
con grazia
rit.
hair.
fair.
fair.
Ah!
Well
may
TRUMPET.
colla voce
a tempo
con grazia
FL.
rit.
men_ make jol-ly O O'er maid - - ens
and_ their fol-ly O!
B
Animato
molto rall.
a tempo
All for a green_ rib - bon to tie in her hair._
Well,
well,
Well,
well,
Well,
well,
Animato
molto rall.
a tempo
TUTTI.

HON.
CHO.
p a tempo
well may men make jol - ly O! And all for a green rib - bon To tie in her
well may men make jol - ly O! Fal la la la la la
men make jol - ly O! Fal la la la la la
sf
pp
a tempo
STGS.
1. & 2.
hair.
la.
la.
f
TRIANG.
1. & 2.
last.
hair To tie in her hair.
la la la la la.
la la la la la.
ENCORE.
DANCE.
BRASS.
p con grazia
STGS.

f p
1.
2. FL.

mf HORN.

STGS.
ppp delicatissimo

C
f
rall.
molto
a tempo ff
BRASS.
TUTTI.
p
HON.
CHO.
ppp
(Honour tacet ad lib.)
ppp delicato
ppp delicato
Well may
Well may
Well may
ppp
STGS. WOOD. HORN.
men make jol-ly O! O'er maid - - ens and their
men make jol-ly O! O'er maid - - ens and their
men make jol-ly O! O'er maid - - ens and their

D (Honour sing.)
HON.
CHO.
fol-ly O! All for a green rib-bon to tie in her hair. Well,
fol-ly O!
Well
fol-ly O!
Well
TUTTI.
well, well may men make jol-ly O! And all for a green rib-bon to
well, well may men make jol-ly O! Fal la la la
may men make jol-ly O! Fal la la la
a tempo
tie in her hair, To tie in her hair.
la la la, la la la la.
la la la, la la la la.
pp a tempo
STGS.
BRASS.
Ped.
*

No. 20. SONG.-(Tom.)

"IF LOVE'S CONTENT."

cue. TOM:—"I cannot find words to speak my passion."

TOM.
more ac - com-plish'd tongue than mine Be el - o -
TOM.
-quent, and I re - main un - heard Where fac - ile
f (VIO.I. WITH VOICE.)
A
dim.
p
TOM.
wit o'er hum-bler gifts doth shine. I have no wealth of
FL.
dim.
p
TOM.
words- no cour-tier's art, With store of hon - ey'd speech my love to

TOM.
f
greet; And can no more than bring a beat - ing
f

TOM.
heart, And, ask - ing no - thing, lay it at her
p

B (Not too slow.) = 88.
accel. rit. p a tempo
TOM.
feet. Come then, for - tune or
accel. rit. p a tempo
STGS. WOOD. HORN.

TOM.
ill be - fall, Go heart, wav - er - ing ne - ver;

TOM.
And if she deem the off-er-ing small, Yet will I love her
BRASS.

Animato.
TOM.
ev-er! Come, then, hap-pi-ness or des-pair, It
f

Tempo I.
TOM.
ask-eth no-thing but to live and die for her
STGS.
WOOD.
TUTTI.
f

TOM.

(Con anima.) ♩= 104.
TOM.
pp
If she be kind, and, as may well be-fall,
(Con anima.)
STGS.
p
pp
Seal with her sweet and ro-sy lips my joy,
Then shall I find fair thoughts and speech with-al, And in her
f
hom-age ev-'ry hour em-ploy.
A (2nd Verse.)
p
Her form, her face, her
FL.
p

TOM.
cresc.
beau-ties man-i-fold The ve-ry well-springs of my heart shall
f
stir; Nor time, nor place Shall ev-er me with-hold; My
latest sigh shall be in praise of her
accel.
rit.
ENCORE.
p
B (2nd Verse.)
(Not too slow.) ♩. = 88.
p a tempo
Come then, for-tune or ill be-fall, Go heart, wav-er-ing
pp a tempo
STGS. WOOD. HORN.

TOM.
ne - ver; And if she deem the off - er - ing small, Yet will I love her
BRASS.
Più vivo.
ev - er! Come, then, hap - pi - ness or des - pair, It
TUTTI.
ask - eth no - thing but to live and die for
accel.
sf sf colla voce
Molto allegro.
her.
ff Molto allegro.
sf

Nº 21. BARCAROLLE.— (Trio Female Voices and Chorus)

RECIT and WALTZ SONG.— (Sophia.)

cue. PARTRIDGE:—"I can't let her get away with this news. Honour!"

1st Sop.
grove
At - tune their notes for ears po -
2nd Sop. & Cont.
grove
At - tune their notes for ears po -
E'en as the birds in yon - der grove
At - tune their
FL.OB.
CL.
1st Sop.
- lite
So let the words We
2nd Sop. & Cont.
- lite
So let the
notes for ears po - lite
So let the words We
FL. OB.
VIO.I.
STGS. WOOD. HORN.
B
1st Sop.
sing of love Be on - ly such as
2nd Sop. & Cont.
sing of love Be on - ly such as

1st Sop.
gen - tle thoughts in - vite,
Lest they her
gen - tle thoughts in - vite, such thoughts in - vite
Lest they her
2nd Sop. & Cont.
gen - tle thoughts in - vite, such thoughts in - vite, Lest they her
in - no - cence, Lest they her in - no - cence af -
in - no - cence, in - no - cence af -
VIO. I.
-fright. Be - guile, be - guile with mu - sic sweet The charm - èd hour of night, And
of night,
-fright. Be - guile, be - guile with mu - sic sweet The charm - èd hour of night, And
Be - guile, be - guile with mu - sic sweet The charm - èd hour of night, And
CHO.
Be - guile with mu - sic mu - sic sweet The
Be - guile, Be - guile with mu - sic sweet The
FL.

1st Sop.
pile, O pile At Beau - ty's feet Fair flow'rs for her de - light.
Fair flow'rs for her de - light, de-light.
2nd Sop. & Cont.
pile, O pile At Beau - ty's feet Fair flow'rs for her de - light E'en
pile, O pile At Beau - ty's feet Fair flow'rs for her de - light.
CHO.
soft and charm - èd hour of night.
charm - èd hour of night. The
soft and charm - èd hour of night.
D
1st Sop.
E'en as the birds in yon - der grove
E'en as the birds in yon - der grove
2nd Sop. & Cont.
as the birds, E'en as the birds in yon - der
E'en as the birds in yon - der grove
birds
mf
The birds in yon - der
FL.OB.

1st Sop.
At-tune their notes for ears po-lite,
So let the
2nd Sop. & Cont.
At-tune their notes for ears po-lite,
So let the
grove, At-tune their notes for ears po-lite, So let the
So let the
CHO.
At-tune their notes for ears po-lite,
So let the
grove,
So let the songs, So let the
VIO.I.
CL.
FL. OB.
STGS. WOOD. HORN.
E
1st Sop.
words We sing of love Be on-ly such as gen-tle thoughts in-
2nd Sop. & Cont.
words We sing of love Be on-ly such as gen-tle thoughts in-
af-
CHO.
words We sing of love Be on-ly such as gen-tle thoughts in-
words We sing of love Be Lest they her

1st Sop.
2nd Sop. & Cont.
CHO.
-vite,
Lest they her in-no-cence Lest
-vite, Such thoughts in-vite,
Lest they her in-no-cence,
-vite, Such thoughts in-vite,
Lest they her in-no-cence,
-vite,
Lest they her in-no-cence Lest
-vite, Such thoughts in-vite,
Lest they her in-no-cence,
in-no-cence,
Lest they her in-no-cence,
VIO.I.
F
they her in-no-cence af-fright, Be-guile, be-
in-no-cence af-fright, Be-guile, be-
they her in-no-cence Be-guile, be-
in-no-cence af-fright, Be-guile, be-
in-no-cence af-fright, Be-guile, be-
OB. SOLO.

1st Sop.
-guile with mu - sic sweet, Be - guile, be - guile, The
2nd Sop. & Cont.
-guile with mu - sic sweet, Be-guile be-guile The
-guile with mu - sic sweet, Be - guile, be - guile, The
CHO.
-guile with mu - sic sweet, Be-guile, be - guile, The
-guile with mu - sic sweet, Be - guile, be - guile, The
1st Sop.
rit.
pp
soft and charm - èd hour of night.
2nd Sop. & Cont.
soft and charm - ed hour of night.
soft and charm - èd hour of night.
CHO.
soft and charm - ed hour of night.
molto accel.
rit.
f
ff
BRASS.
TIMP.

(Enter Sophia, in barge.)
G
Allegro risoluto. Broadly.
CHO.
Hail, Hail! to the Fair! Hail, Hail! to the Fair!
Hail, Hail! to the Fair! Hail, Hail! to the Fair!
ff Broadly.
a tempo
(Sophia comes down Stage.)
Hail! to the Fair!
CHO.
Hail! to the Fair!
a tempo
rall.
marcato
TRUMPET.
SO.
VIO.I.
H
RECIT.
SO.
Which is my own true self,
rit.
p
ad lib. throughout.

a tempo

SO.

I, who here to-night Do stand a-mazed To find a world so

STGS. HORN.

f a tempo

SO.

Recit.

bright? ___ Or she who crept Last night her pil-low to, And

FL.

SO.

a tempo

slept and wept The hours al-ter-nate through? Or

STGS.

pp

mf

J *Risoluto*

SO.

I, or she, Wak-ing will prove a-non; An this a dream be,

accel.

PIZZ.

3

f BRASS.

ARCO

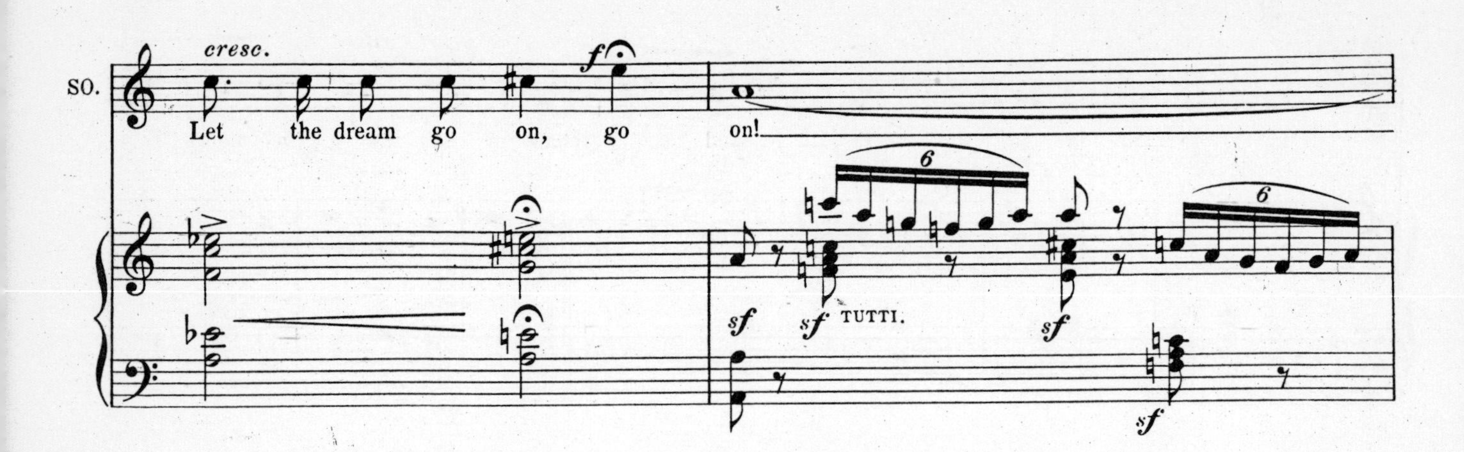
cresc.
SO.
Let the dream go on, go on!
TUTTI.

Allegro molto. (a lá Valse) 𝅗𝅥. = 80.
SO.
Ah!
TUTTI.
cresc.

With great spirit.
SO.
For to - night,
STGS.
With great spirit.

SO.
for to - night Let me dream out my dream of de - light, Tra la la la la la

SO.

rit.

la la — la la la la — And — purchase of sor-row a mo-ment's re -

rit.

M
SO.
swing Be-tween mad-ness And glad-ness To - night.
FL. OB.

SO.
My eyes are daz-zled and dazed with a strange de-
mf
p

SO.
-light. I am dazed like a lark that has gazed On the sun
f
BRASS.
f
p

N
con grazia
SO.
in his flight. Ah! Ah! Ah!
PIZZ.
HORN.
sf
pp con grazia
TRIANG.

SO.
Ah
Ah

O
sf
SO.
Ah
f
TUTTI.

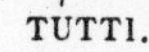
ENCORE

SO.

P
SO.
For to - night, for to - night, Let me
sf
f
p

SO.
dream out my dream of de-light, Tra la la la la la la la la la
STGS.

SO.
Q
rit.
f
la la And pur-chase of sor-row a mo-ment's re-spite I am
rit.
f
TUTTI.

SO.
a tempo
accel.
dazed Like a lark that has gazed On the sun in his
a tempo
p
accel.

SO.
f
R
flight. Ah For I
STGS. FL.
f
p

SO.
wa - ver and swing Be - tween mad - ness And glad - ness To - night! Let me
sing, Ah!
accel.
pp
accel.
'Twixt mad - ness and glad - ness to - night, to -
accel. molto
lunga
sf
f
ff
Ped.
TUTTI.
- night!
Presto.

Nº 22.
TRIO.-(Honour, Partridge and Gregory.)
cue. PARTRIDGE:- "Gregory, I will be the father of your children."
♩= 126.
Allegro con brio.
Honour.
Partridge.
Gregory.
Allegro con brio.
TUTTI.
Piano.
STGS.
HON.
1. Says a well-worn Saw, and a deep one, And lov-ers be-lieve it
2. "As you make your bed you must lie there" An-o-ther old Saw doth
PAR.
GRE.
CL. WITH VOICE.
pp
true, That what's e-nough to keep one Is ev-er e-nough for
say. Then do not wake-ful sigh there But mer-ri-ly snore a-

A
HON.
two, Is ev-er e - nough for two.
-way, But mer-ri-ly snore a - way.
PAR.
If that be true, E -
And thank-ful be E -
GRE.
If that be true, E -
And thank-ful be E -
PICC.
S.DRUM.
HON.
PAR.
-nough for two Is log-ic-al-ly plen-ty For four, And thus 'Tis
-ter-nal-ly, That straw is cheap and plen-ty, When joys do come Ad
GRE.
-nough for two Is log-ic-cal-ly, plen-ty For four, And thus 'Tis
-ter-nal-ly, That straw is cheap and plen-ty, When joys do come Ad
BRASS.
HON.
PAR.
plain to us We might go on, We might go on, go on, go on, go
lib-i-tum, They may go on, They may go on, go on, go on, go
GRE.
plain to us We might go on, We might go on, go on, go on, go
lib-i-tum, They may go on, They may go on, go on, go on, go
FAG.

rit.
HON.
Ah!
Ah!
PAR.
on, go on, We might go on to twenty! Ah!
on, go on, They may go on to twenty! Ah!
GRE.
on, go on, We might go on to twenty! Ah!
on, go on, They may go on to twenty! Ah!
sf rit.
TUTTI.
B
Con grazia.
HON.
Saws, Saws, Wise old Saws, Give them all their due, And
PAR.
GRE.
Con grazia.
pp STGS. CL.
TRIANG.
C
HON.
let us pay Res - pect to - day Their an - cient wis - dom to.
PAR.
GRE.
FL.

HON.
Pause, pause, Seek not flaws, Let ripe old age con - tent 'ee;
PAR.
Pause, pause, Seek not flaws, Let ripe old age con - tent 'ee;
GRE.
Pause, pause, Seek not flaws, Let ripe old age con - tent 'ee;
HON.
Bow to them, And pass them Nem - i - ne dis-sen-ti - en - te.
PAR.
Bow to them, And pass them Nem - i - ne dis-sen-ti - en - te.
GRE.
Bow to them, And pass them Nem - i - ne dis-sen-ti - en - te.
1.
f
2. accel.
HON.
-te, Nem - i - ne dis - sen - ti - en - te.
accel.
PAR.
-te, Nem - i - ne dis - sen - ti - en - te.
accel.
GRE.
-te, Nem - i - ne dis - sen - ti - en - te.
2.
accel.
STGS. WOOD. HORNS.
PIZZ.
f

ENCORE.

DANCE.

No. 22a MELOS.

Cue:– LADY BELLASTON. "Who has been an object of my charity."

No. 23. FINALE—ACT III.

cue. SOPHIA:—"I dare not be guilty of disobedience."

SO.
HON.
TOM.
FL.
TRIANG.
p
ARCO
Quick! you maids with cheeks like ros - es, Go you, ga - ther
EE
pret - ty pos - ies; Hale the hap - py man a - long
Ding, dong, ding,
HORN.
Ding dong.
Bring his wav' - ring mind to rea - son,
dong, ding, ding - a - dong, dong.
sfp

SO.
HON.
Hy - men's nev - er out of sea - son, Wed - ding bells,
TOM.
SO.
HON.
wed - ding bells Ring aye the same
TOM.
f
Ding, dong, ding,
SO.
rit.
For
HON.
rit.
Ding, dong, Ding, dong, ding, dong, ding, dong
TOM.
rit.
dong, ding, ding - a - dong, dong, Ding, dong, ding, dong, ding, dong
rit.

FF
a tempo
SO.
Lord and La - dy, Squire and Dame, Good - man Gos - sip, Hodge and Au - drey.
HON.
Ding dong Ding dong
TOM.
Ding dong Ding dong
CHO.
Lord and La - dy, Squire and Dame, Good - man Gos - sip, Hodge and Au - drey.
Ding dong Ding dong
STGS. WOOD. HORN.
a tempo
TRIANG.
SO.
Ah!
HON.
Come, you swains and dam - o - sels Keep the mer - ry mar - riage bells
TOM.
Come, you swains and dam - o - sels Keep the mer - ry mar - riage bells
CHO.
Come, you swains and dam - o - sels Keep the mer - ry mar - riage bells
Come, you swains and dam - o - sels Keep the mer - ry mar - riage bells
TUTTI.
PIZZ.

SO.
Ring-ing, ring-ing, ring-ing, ring-ing, Dong ding dong,
HON.
Ring-ing, ring-ing, ring-ing, ring-ing, Dong ding dong,
TOM.
Ring-ing, ring-ing, ring-ing, ring-ing, Dong ding dong,
CHO.
Ring-ing, ring-ing, ring-ing, ring-ing, Dong ding dong,
Ring-ing, ring-ing, ring-ing, ring-ing, Dong ding dong,
FL.
sf
GG
SO.
Ring the mer-ry, mer-ry, mer-ry mar-riage bells. Ring the
HON.
Ring the mer-ry, mer-ry, mer-ry mar-riage bells. Ring the
TOM.
Ring the mer-ry, mer-ry, mer-ry mar-riage bells. Ring the
Pesante.
ff
CHO.
Ring the mer-ry, mer-ry, mer-ry mar-riage bells. Ding dong ding dong. Ring the
ff
Ring the mer-ry, mer-ry, mer-ry mar-riage bells. Ding dong ding dong.
Pesante.
ff
TUTTI.

SO.
mer - ry, mer - ry bells. Ring the
HON.
mer - ry, mer - ry bells. Ring the
TOM.
mer - ry, mer - ry bells. Ring the
mer - ry, mer - ry bells. Ding dong ding dong. Ring the
CHO.
ding - a - dong Ding dong ding dong.
HH
SO.
mer - ry, mer - ry bells. Ding Dong Ding
HON.
mer - ry, mer - ry bells. Ding dong Ding dong Ding
TOM.
mer - ry, mer - ry bells. Ding dong ding dong ding dong ding dong ding
ding dong ding dong ding
mer - ry, mer - ry bells. Ding dong ding dong ding dong ding dong ding
CHO.
Ding dong ding dong ding
ding - a - dong Ding dong, ding dong ding dong ding dong ding
ff

lunga pausa
SO.
Ring out the mar - riage bells Ding dong ding
HON.
dong, Ring out the mar - riage bells Ding dong ding
TOM.
dong, Ring out the mar - riage bells Ding dong ding
CHO.
dong, Ring out the mar - riage bells Ding dong ding
dong, Ring out the mar - riage bells Ding dong ding
lunga pausa
Presto.
dong.
ff
With a
dong.
With a
dong.
With a
dong.
With a
dong.
With a
Presto.

PRINCIPALS with CHORUS.
JIG. (Presto.)
CHO.
fal la la la la la la la
fal la la la la la la la
ff
la With a fal la la la la la la la
la With a fal la la la la la la la
JJ
1.
2.
la With a la.
la With a la.
ff
ff
sff

Curtain.
CHO.
sf
accel.
poco
a
poco
lunga pausa
sff
Ped.
END OF OPERA

THE EMERALD ISLE

OR

THE CAVES OF CARRIG-CLEENA

WRITTEN BY
BASIL HOOD

COMPOSED BY
ARTHUR SULLIVAN & EDWARD GERMAN

VOCAL SCORE
VOCAL SCORE (Concert Version)
PIANOFORTE SOLO
LIBRETTO

THE TYPICAL IRISH PAT.
WHEN ALFRED'S FRIENDS.
OH, SETTING SUN.
IT'S IRELAND WHERE YOU'LL FIND HIM.
IMITATIONS.
GOOD-BYE, MY NATIVE TOWN.
THE LITTLE WOODEN SOLDIER.
I LOVE YOU, MY DARLIN'.

VALSE ... ... Arranged by CARL KIEFERT
LANCERS ... ... Arranged by WARWICK WILLIAMS
Also for Full and Small Orchestra.

GODFREY'S PIANOFORTE SELECTION (Solo or Duet).
Also for Full and Small Orchestra and Military Band.

J. E. NEWELL'S VIOLIN AND PIANOFORTE SELECTION.

CHAPPELL & CO. Ltd. 50, NEW BOND STREET, LONDON, W.1
NEW YORK — SYDNEY

MERRIE ENGLAND

A Comic Opera in Two Acts

WRITTEN BY
BASIL HOOD

COMPOSED BY
EDWARD GERMAN

VOCAL SCORE
VOCAL SCORE (Concert Version)
CHORUSES

PIANOFORTE SOLO
LIBRETTO
CHORUSES (S.S.A.)

THE YEOMEN OF ENGLAND (In C and D.)
LOVE IS MEANT TO MAKE US GLAD (In D flat, E flat and F)
O PEACEFUL ENGLAND
THE ENGLISH ROSE (Song) (G and B flat)
LOVE IS MEANT TO MAKE US GLAD (Quintet, Quartet, or Trio, octavo)

WALTZ SONG
SHE HAD A LETTER FROM HER LOVE
COME TO ARCADIE (Duet)
IT IS THE MERRY MONTH OF MAY (Duet)
IN ENGLAND, MERRIE ENGLAND (Quartet, octavo)

LONG LIVE ELIZABETH (S.A.T.B., S.S.A, S.A., T.T.B.B.) (Arranged for Military Band and Brass Band)
O PEACEFUL ENGLAND (S.A.T.B., S.A.)
THE YEOMEN OF ENGLAND (T.T.B.B.)
THE ENGLISH ROSE (S.S.A.)

FIRST PIANOFORTE SELECTION
SECOND PIANOFORTE SELECTION
Also for Full or Small Orchestra and Military Band

VALSE .. .. Arranged by CARL KIEFERT
LANCERS .. .. Arranged by WARWICK WILLIAMS
Also for Full or Small Orchestra

FOUR DANCES (Piano Solo or Duet) .. .. Arranged by the COMPOSER
FOUR DANCES (Violin and Piano) .. .. Arranged by the COMPOSER
SIX EASY PIECES (Piano Solo) .. .. Arranged by T. F. DUNHILL

TOLHURST'S VIOLIN AND PIANOFORTE SELECTION

CHAPPELL & CO. LTD. 50 NEW BOND STREET, LONDON, W.1
NEW YORK · TORONTO · SYDNEY · PARIS

No. 2589

272

THE REBEL MAID

A Romantic Light Opera.

Book by
ALEX. M. THOMPSON and GERALD DODSON.
Lyrics by
GERALD DODSON.
Music by
MONTAGUE F. PHILLIPS.

Vocal Score (Complete.)
Vocal Score (Concert Version.)

Separate **VOCAL NUMBERS** *may be had as follows:*

THE FISHERMEN OF ENGLAND (In B♭ and C)
SAIL MY SHIPS
ARE MY LANTERNS SHINING?
WHEN A DREAM OF LOVE YOU CHERISH
THE OLD-FASHIONED CLOAK
HOME AGAIN
SHEPHERDESS AND BEAU BROCADE. (Quartet) S.A.T.B.
HOW STRANGE THIS TUMULT. (Madrigal) S.A.T.B
WISDOM AND FOLLY. (Unaccompanied Madrigal) S.A.T.B.

PIANOFORTE ARRANGEMENTS.

THE REBEL MAID VALSE
THE REBEL MAID GAVOTTE
THE REBEL MAID SELECTION
FOUR DANCES from "The Rebel Maid." (Arranged by the Composer).

CHAPPELL & CO., LTD.,
50, NEW BOND STREET, LONDON, W.1.
NEW YORK. —— SYDNEY.
And may be had of all Music Sellers.

A Princess of Kensington

A COMIC OPERA, IN THREE ACTS

LYRICS BY
BASIL HOOD

MUSIC BY
EDWARD GERMAN

VOCAL SCORE

VOCAL SCORE (Concert Version)

PIANOFORTE SOLO

LIBRETTO

A SPRIG OF ROSEMARIE. (In D, E flat, and F.)
FOUR JOLLY SAILORMEN. (In C and D.)
TWIN BUTTERFLIES.
WHERE HAVEN LIES.
OH, WHAT IS WOMAN'S DUTY.
THE HAPPY MEAN.
HE WAS A SIMPLE SAILORMAN.
SEVEN O'CLOCK IN THE MORNING. (Duet.)
FOUR JOLLY SAILORMEN. (Quartet.)
WHO THAT KNOWS HOW I LOVE YOU. (Sextet.) Octavo.

LANCERS ... ... Arranged by DAN GODFREY.

SELECTION FOR THE PIANOFORTE ... ... Arranged by DAN GODFREY.
(Also for Full and Small Orchestra, Military Band, and Brass Band.)

CHAPPELL & CO. Ltd. 50, NEW BOND STREET, LONDON, W.1
NEW YORK — SYDNEY

No. 2472